# Old Torry and Aberdeen Ha

## Rosie Nicol and Patricia Newman

Old Torry.

Old Torry in the early 1900s, looking along Sinclair Road from west, with the West Leading Light on the right and the East Leading Light in the distance. The leading lights were installed in 1842 to mark the navigation channel into the harbour. The lights show red when it is safe to enter the harbour and green when it is dangerous. The towers were built of cast iron. At one time there was a keeper of the lights who lived in the cottage next to the West Light. Today the lights are controlled from the Marine Operations Centre across the harbour on North Pier.

A Torry fisher quine wearing a striped cotton apron over a striped woollen skirt, a checked shawl and carrying a traditional wicker woven basket or creel on her back. If she had a large load of fish or if she was taking messages home, she would put a murlan – a small basket – inside or on top of the creel.

## Acknowledgements

Allan Condie for information about ships and railway engines
Ina Gauld for her local knowledge
John Main for his local knowledge, family history and photographs
Chris Croly for his knowledge of Torry
Sandy and Roslyn Bruce for all their help
All the Staff at Aberdeen City Archives, for all their help
George Mauchline, Brian Watt and Eric Lawson for loan of postcards
from their collections

RNLI Aberdeen for their information and hospitality
Shore Porters for their photograph
Keith Donald for his knowledge of Balnagask Golf Course
Ian and Dave for their support and encouragement!
Richard Stenlake for giving us this opportunity!

# INTRODUCTION

Aberdeen was created a Royal Burgh by King David I (1124–53) and was a centre for maritime trade from early times. It was an important trading city for the members of the Hanseatic League whose members included Bruges, Lubeck, Danzig, Riga and Novgorod. Although Aberdeen was a port in early times, it was not a fishing port. This function was fulfilled by Fittie (or Footdee) on the northern bank of the estuary of the River Dee and Torry (Upper and Lower) on the south bank. These were distinct communities at that time.

Lower Torry developed into what became known as Old Torry. Fittie was originally sited beside St Clement's Church but a new development of squares in what was known as The Sandness was built for the fisher folk in the early 1800s.

Torry was originally in Kincardineshire and was owned by the Abbey of Arbroath from the 12th century until 1560. Its importance was confirmed when it was created a Burgh of Barony in 1495 by King James IV, allowing it to trade freely and to hold markets and an annual fair. Travel from the south to Aberdeen was impeded by the River Dee until the first Bridge of Dee was constructed in 1520 with a substantial legacy from Bishop Elphinstone and a large contribution from Bishop Gavin Dunbar. Although this bridge facilitated travel to Aberdeen, it isolated Torry. The building of the Wellington Suspension Bridge, locally known as the Chain Briggie, was built in 1830 in place of the Craiglug Ferry to link Torry and Aberdeen. This bridge was much closer to Torry but the ferries were still the transport of choice for locals.

Torry was amalgamated into the City of Aberdeen in 1891. Around half of the area of Torry was owned by the Menzies family of Pitfodels with the remainder owned by the City of Aberdeen.

The River Dee Estuary took water from the Denburn, the Millburn and the Pow Creek all of which entered it on the Aberdeen bank of the Dee and helped to form Aberdeen Harbour. The entrance to the harbour tended to silt up and was even blocked on several occasions. John Smeaton designed a pier on the north bank of the estuary which was finished in 1780 and with additions and modifications has helped provide a safe harbour for Aberdeen.

Shore Porters (originally called Pynours) carried goods from the harbours of Aberdeen and Fittie. Poynernook behind South Market Street is a reminder of their original name. They were already established in 1498 when they were mentioned in council minutes. Formed to give protection to their members, they were probably the first co-operative in the world. In a charter of 1707, Queen Anne confirmed the Pynour Craft to be porters and carriers from the ships in the harbour – then at the foot of Shore Brae – up to Aberdeen. In the charter, mention is made of previous rights and privileges granted to the Pynours by King William the Lion who reigned from 1165 to 1214.

A lifeboat was first established in Aberdeen in 1802 by the Harbour Commissioners. In addition to the lifeboat, rocket-propelled life-saving equipment was available on the North Pier, to operate north of the River Dee, and also at Torry for areas south of the Dee. In 1925, the Royal National Lifeboat Institution took over the operation of both the lifeboats and the rocket life-saving apparatus.

Shipbuilding was carried out in Aberdeen and Torry by various family firms. Among the most notable were Duthie, Hall, Hood, Lewis and Hall Russell. They built around 3,000 ships of all sizes from the early 1800s to the demise of the last yard in 1992.

In order to further improve the harbour at Aberdeen, a great work of diverting the channel of the River Dee was undertaken in 1871. This work involved the demolition of a large part of Old Torry and the purchase of the rights of salmon fishers on the Dee.

A proposal for the building of a bridge from Aberdeen to Torry was promulgated in 1871 but it took a disaster in 1876 for the building of the Victoria Bridge to go ahead. A ferry carrying holidaymakers to and from Aberdeen across the harbour mouth to Torry capsized with the loss of 33 lives. The ferryman was charged with culpable homicide and culpable neglect of duty by allowing the ferry to be overcrowded among other failings. He died before he could be brought to court.

Whaling began in Aberdeen in 1753 but was not particularly successful in the early days. However, by 1850 there was a considerable fleet sailing to Greenland. The oil was used to light lamps, prior to the introduction of coal gas, and the whalebone was used in corsets. The *Oscar*, a whaling ship from Aberdeen, was wrecked off Girdleness in 1813 with the loss of 43 lives. Oscar Road in Torry was named after the ship and in memory of the men lost. The lighthouse at Girdleness was erected following the wreck of the *Oscar*. However, by 1853, there were only two Aberdeen whaling ships and by the 1890s only Dundee had a whaling fleet.

# INTRODUCTION CONTINUED

Traditionally, boats from Fittie and Torry would fish with lines for the abundant white fish in the North Sea. White fishing involved the whole family; children would gather mussels and women would spend many hours each day baiting lines, gutting the catch and taking it to market.In 1835, Aberdeen Town Council considered setting up a station for herring fishing. The first season, in 1836, was very successful and led to great prosperity for the city and for Torry. As herring lived in shoals, netting was much more practical than line fishing. The fishing fleet depended on the quality of their nets and the repair and maintenance of the nets fell mostly to their womenfolk. In the 1880s, steam took over from sail and transformed the fishing industry. Thousands of people flocked to Torry in search of work in fishing and ancillary industries. While the men fished, the women gutted, salted and packed the herring into barrels ready for distant markets.

From 1880s onwards, Aberdeen and Torry experienced a boom in steam trawling leading to a huge influx of families associated with fishing and boat building. Between 1881 and 1901 the population of Torry rose from 1,117 to 9,386, so houses were required to accommodate these several thousand people. There was a great property boom, with dozens of tenements built in Victoria Road, Walker Road, Menzies Road, Grampian Road and other shorter streets most of which are still occupied over 100 years later.

The prosperity of Aberdeen and Torry has always been linked to the sea and as such has benefited from trading vessels, a fishing fleet and in the 20th and 21st centuries from the establishment of offshore oil support industries and from an expansion of container traffic.The modern Aberdeen Harbour has a major financial impact on Aberdeen, handling around 4 million tons of cargo and bringing continued financial stability to the area.

Old Torry. Aberdeen.

Old Torry in the early 1900s, looking along Sinclair Road from the East Leading Light to the West Leading Light. The small building beyond the East Light was a public toilet, known locally as "the Torry Parliament"! The building with a turreted roof was the Torry Bar, at the junction with Baxter Street, still there today, but boarded up. The houses beyond the toilet are in Pierhead and Sinclair Row. 1898 – 1899 valuation rolls show that all these houses except one were occupied by fishermen, the exception being a barrel maker. Other streets in Old Torry were Ferry Road, Sinclair Row, Sinclair Place, Ferry Place, Fore Close and Back Close.

OLD TORRY, ABERDEEN

Torry developed as two villages, Upper and Nether Torry. It was from Nether Torry that the village known as Old Torry developed in the late 18th and early 19th century. Old Torry is no longer a residential village. Many cottages were demolished when the course of the River Dee was diverted in 1871. The remainder disappeared in 1970s as the oil industry developed, with Torry Quay required for industrial use.

The Harbour, Old Torry

Old Torry Harbour in the early 1900s. This view is from north side of the harbour looking south to fishing boats in Old Torry Harbour, with village beyond. The Torry Bar is to right of picture, eastern Leading Light to the left.

This picture looking up Victoria Road near the junction with Sinclair Road to the left and Menzies Road to the right was taken around 1909. In the late 19th century, as fishing and industry developed in Aberdeen, there was a need for more land for building houses and industrial premises. After some very controversial debate, a private company, The City of Aberdeen Land Association, purchased the land previously occupied by Torry Farm. Victoria Road was one of the first streets to be developed when 'new' Torry began to grow from Victoria Bridge southwards and was built as a "spine" running through Torry, with other streets running off like "ribs". After Victoria Road, the next streets to develop were Menzies Road and Walker Road.

The bow-fronted shop with tenement flats above is 53-55 Victoria Road, built in 1890s for George Coutts, grocer which has continued to be a grocer's shop for over 100 years. After Mr Coutts' day it became Nuttens and now it is Taylors. When first built, part of the building was rented to Guilianotti's Ice Cream shop. Beyond Coutts' shop were a dairy, a watchmaker and a cycle agent and ironmonger. On the opposite corner is the Victoria Bar beyond which other shops included clothier, draper, chemist, post office and several departments of the Northern Co-operative Ltd. – boots and shoes, drapers, butchers, bakers and grocers. The people of Torry were well-served with all sorts of shops and facilities. Torry had its own fire station and police station on the Torry side of Victoria Bridge. Trams were run by Aberdeen Corporation from 1898. By 1902 all trams in Aberdeen were electric rather than horse-drawn and the Torry route, from Guild Street to St Fittick's Road, opened on 10th October 1903.

Looking up Victoria Road with Grampian Road off to the right, just before the First World War. The new tenements of Torry had a wide range of owners, many associated with fishing, shipbuilding and shipping, who in turn rented the flats to folk employed in local industries. The rules for building, maintaining and inhabiting tenements were numerous and laid down in Title Deeds. For example, owners were prohibited from quarrying for clay on the site, and from erecting a tannery, brewery, distillery, or workshops for masons, wrights, smiths, coopers, weavers, candle makers or indeed a slaughterhouse! The production and/or selling of alcoholic liquor was also forbidden. Title Deeds could also specify that buildings could be built only from local granite, and laid down the responsibilities of repairing and maintaining tenements. This was relatively easy when whole tenements were owned by and let out by the same person. It became more complicated when responsibilities became shared between several owners. Unlike other cities in Scotland, Aberdeen does not have a history of factors who are responsible for repairs and maintenance of communal blocks. Despite national legislation, communal repairs are still a major problem.

The majority of tenements had at least six flats, some eight, depending whether shops were included at ground level. Most had no bathrooms and shared flush toilets on the ground floor and on stair landings. Usually, each flat had a shed either in the back yard or in cellars below the tenements and each tenement had a shared wash house with boiler and sink. Many tenements had communal lofts and uniquely to Aberdeen many of these were floored when built and used as drying lofts for drying washing and for storage. Tenements had strict rules for communal living. Tenants had to take their turn at cleaning the stairs and each would have a specific day for using the wash house, drying green or loft.

Between 1881 and 1901, with the growth of fishing and shipbuilding industries, the population of Torry rose from 1,117 to 9,386, so many new houses were required. The majority of the streets branching off Victoria Road were built as tenements – blocks of six or eight flats, with shared stairways, gardens, toilets and wash-houses. Shops and business premises, with smart shopfronts, were included on the ground floors of some of these tenements.

Records from 1910 show that 7 Menzies Road, on the left of the picture, had two shops and six flats, and was built in 1902 for a total cost of £1,750. It had pitch pine fittings on the communal stairs and WCs on landings. Menzies Road is one of the larger streets with over 50 tenements on each side of the road. Valuation Rolls from 1906 show that the business premises on the left hand side of this picture included the Victoria Bar, a restaurant, a doctor, a newsagent and tobacconist and a Lipton's ham and butter merchants. On the right hand side of the street were grocers, fishmonger, dairy, butcher and Allan's "Public Supply Stores". Sadly these shops fell into decline in the late 20th century but in 2011 they were refurbished and re-opened as part of a regeneration scheme, Torry Rocks, giving people the chance to open up new businesses.

An early 1900s view along Walker Road from its junction with Victoria Road. On right hand corner is Mrs Williams's draper and milliners shop advertising "Hooks and Eyes". High up on the same tenement is an advert for Cocoa. At the corner on the left is a chemist's shop, with pestle and mortar on the wall. This shop is still a pharmacy today. Records from 1906 showed that the two storey houses on the right hand side of Walker Road belonged to prosperous folk - fish and granite merchants. The children could be from either Walker Road School which is just out of shot, or Victoria Road School which is further up Victoria Road to the left. Perhaps though, they could be Sunday school pupils, as the street is devoid of traffic.

*Grampian Road, Torry*

A picture taken in the first decade of the 20th century, looking east down Grampian Road towards Victoria Road with Glenbervie Road going uphill on the right. The four tenements on the right hand side of Grampian Road leading round to several tenements on Glenbervie Road were all built by local builder John Park who lived in nearby Menzies Road. The flats on the corner were built with bathrooms, a rarity in Torry tenements!

The arched building facing us is the rear of Torry Library which fronts onto Victoria Road. It was designed by Messrs Brown and Watt Architects and built at a cost of approximately £1500. The reading room was opened on 19th December 1902 by Provost James Walker. Initially, as it was not a lending library, members would request books which would be fetched from the Central Library on Rosemount Viaduct in Aberdeen by a man with a hand cart. The reading room was a great success from the start and Torry Library, in its original building is still a popular community resource today. The mound of earth on the right is the bank in front of Sacred Heart Roman Catholic Church which was opened for worship in 1911.

These four handsome tenements with fine views over Aberdeen are numbers 107 to 113 Grampian Road and their names - *Glenbirnie House, Glenesk House, Glentanar House* and *Glenlivet House* - are painted on the fanlight windows over the front doors. The middle two blocks, *Glentanar House* and *Glenesk House* were built circa 1905 by Richard Lewis, son of John Lewis shipbuilder and brother of Sir Andrew Lewis. In 1906 *Glenbirnie House* was added by James Gow, a tinsmith, and then Richard Lewis added *Glenlivet House* a year later. The "unfinished" look to the gables suggests that there may have been plans to build another tenement which were never realised. Unlike many tenements in Torry, these were built with bathrooms. Despite their superior facilities, the total rateable value in 1905-1906 for *Glentanar House* and *Glenesk House* was just £144!

Torry's first school was opened near Nigg Kirk in January 1849, with Mr Barnet as headmaster. The local fishermen's association helped to build a replacement, Torry Public School on Abbey Road which was opened in May 1873. As the population grew in size there was a need to expand the school. In 1905 the old Torry Public School was extended considerably, at a cost of £8700, and renamed Victoria Road Primary School.

Walker Road, Torry. Aberdeen.

Looking west along Walker Road from Victoria Road with the imposing new granite-built school on the left and sweeping rows of tenements on the right. Walker Road School opened on 8th March 1897 with nearly 600 pupils on the roll to accommodate the growing numbers of children now living in Torry's new tenements.

The Education (Scotland) Act 1872 made education compulsory and the Scottish Education Department took over the running of schools from the Church of Scotland. Burgh as well as parish schools now came under school boards run by local committees.

St Fittick's Old Church was the original church in the area, near the Bay of Nigg, where there had been a church since the thirteenth century. Designed by the architect John Smith it was the parish kirk from 1716 until 1829 when it was replaced by Nigg Parish Church. The church is of perpendicular Gothic design and is rectangular with a stone built square tower at the west built with decorative contrasting detail and corner buttresses.

As Torry grew it was clear that Nigg Parish Church was inconvenient for the new centre of poulation and in 1898 work began on a new St Fittick's Church in Walker Road, which is the present day Parish Church of Torry. St Fittick's old churchyard continued to be used as a cemetery until the early 20th century and the ruins of the old church can still be visited today.

A. 2976.                                    Victoria Road from the West, Torry.

In this 1935 photo the tram-lines are still in place, but buses are visible in the distance. The church on the right was built by the Free Church congregation, and opened its doors in 1890. In 1898 church halls were erected and then a back gallery was added in 1903 to accommodate the growing congregation. After several amalgamations and splits in the congregation it became a Church of Scotland church in 1930 and continued as such until the 1990s when it was deconsecrated. It currently houses play facilities for children.

Victoria Road looking west. The tenements on the left were fronted by cast iron railings which enclosed the front gardens and basement areas of many of Aberdeen's Georgian and Victorian buildings. Unfortunately many of these were removed during the Second World War, to help the war effort. The building with arched windows on the centre right of the picture is St Peter's Episcopal Church. The advent of steam trawling brought hundreds of fishermen to Aberdeen and to Torry looking for jobs many of whom were Episcopalians and led to a need for a new church. At first a temporary mission hall was hired in 1882. Eventually building work started on a new church in Victoria Road in 1897. The church building was converted into sheltered housing in the 1990s. The congregation now meets in the church hall at the rear of the former church.

A feature of St Peter's Church was a model boat, commissioned by the congregation from James Cordiner's boat yard on the banks of the Dee and named the A153 St Peter and St Andrew. Celebrating the link between the church and fishing it hung from the roof of the church and measured 15 feet in length.

Sacred Heart Roman Catholic Church, at 15 Grampian Road on the corner of Glenbervie Road cost £4,000 to build and had an initial seating capacity of 350. It opened on 19th November 1911 when High Mass was celebrated by Bishop Chisholm. It was designed by Charles Jean Menart, a Belgian architect and graduate of Glasgow College of Art and built by David Weir of Claremont Street, Aberdeen. The church was built mainly of red Clinterty granite in random freestone rubble and has regularly shaped ashlar quoin stones, lintels, string course and skews. The roof is of red English tiles. The random construction of the walls is a testament to the skill of the masons. The design is Romanesque, having robust walls, semicircular window arches and grouped windows under a larger arch. The roofline and tower of this B listed building are typically French Romanesque while the tall windows are reminiscent of a more Germanic Romanesque style.

A. 2975.    Wellington Bridge from the Esplanade, Torry.

The Wellington Suspension Bridge was opened in 1831 at a narrow crossing point of the Dee to link Ferryhill and Torry and replaced the Craiglug or Upper Ferry. The bridge was designed by Samuel Brown RN who invented this type of chain bridge. The then City Architect John Smith designed the pylons and octagonal tollhouse. It was built by Messrs Abernethy at their Ferryhill Foundry which was at that time sited just next to the river crossing.

The bridge was refurbished in 1930, but eventually closed to vehicular traffic in 1984 and to pedestrians in 2002. It has since been strengthened and re–opened as a public footbridge. It is a category A listed structure. This view looks across the Dee from Esplanade to Torry, with the tenements of Menzies Road and Craiginches Prison on the skyline. The octagonal tollhouse can just be seen under the tree on the right.

Victoria Road Bridge, viewed from South Esplanade East, Torry, taken before the First World War with the chimneys and spires of Aberdeen in the distance and Ogilvie's Boatyard in the foreground. The building of this bridge was long overdue as the previous crossing from Aberdeen to Torry was by ferry from Pocra Quay. Disaster struck in 1876 when the Dee Ferry Boat sank, with the loss of 32 people. A plaque on the bridge records the ferry disaster.

The bridge was designed by engineer Edward L J Blyth of Edinburgh and opened in 1881, well-timed for the expansion of Torry. It formed an important link between Market Street Aberdeen and Victoria Road, Torry. It still bridges the Dee today, and was listed category B in 1967.

Craiginches Prison is on the left, with the tenements of Walker Road on the right. The prison which overlooks the river Dee was built in 1890 at a cost of £36,000. Valuation rolls for 1900 show that the prison building included eleven houses; accommodation for governor, matron and warders. It is a medium security prison, with a design capacity of 155 and is contracted to hold up to 230 prisoners. All maintenance work in the prison is carried out by staff and prisoners. Henry John Burnett, the last man to be executed in Scotland, was hanged inside the prison for murder on 15th August 1963.

All the vacant land in foreground has since been used for housing.

At the crossroads in the early 1900s with Market Street ahead and behind, Guild Street to the left and Trinity Quay to the right. The small building on the right is the Weighbridge Office - the weighbridge was an essential part of cargo operations on the docks. The building behind the Weighbridge Office on corner of Trinity Quay and Market Street has had a variety of uses including as a "dole" office and a casino. On the opposite corner is the Temperance Hotel, where no alcohol was served.

Market Street was laid out in 1842 and got its name from the "New Market" which was designed by Archibald Simpson and in operation until 1971. Guild Street is the home of Aberdeen's Tivoli Theatre, built in 1872 and formerly known as "Her Majesty's Theatre". It was named after William Guild (1586–1657) a Scottish minister, academic and theological writer.

333 Market Street and The Harbour, Aberdeen "Adelphi Series"

A Torry bound tram passes the activity on South Market Street with colliers at the quay unloading coal onto horse-drawn carts for local merchants. Trinity and Regent Quays are beyond the harbour, with the Town House clock on the horizon. Horse-drawn trams were run by Aberdeen Corporation from 1898, but by 1902 all Aberdeen's trams were electric, and the Torry route opened in 1903. Further down South Market Street was the Torry Tram Depot, at the corner of North Esplanade West, an imposing building, built of pink Corennie granite. Torry's tram route closed in 1931 and bus services took over.

A view from Market Street with one of the Aberdeen Coal & Shipping Company's colliers alongside. This view pre-dates the abandonment of the Torry trams in 1931.The ship is either the *Redhall* of 1917 or the *Ferryhill* of 1919 which were built by Halls of Aberdeen. The *Ferryhill* was sunk by a mine off the Tyne in January 1940 but the *Redhall* continued in service until 1959 when she was replaced by a smaller motor coaster which also took the name *Ferryhill*.

The huts on the quay belonged to coal merchants who used them as bases for their business dealings as boats laden with coal came into harbour. The Harbour Office with its clock tower is on the far side of harbour with the Salvation Army Citadel showing behind. The other big building on the skyline is a tall tenement on Union Street, number 41, which stands two storeys above its neighbours and today houses several company offices and the Citizens Advice Bureau.

INSTITUTE OF THE ROYAL NATIONAL MISSION TO DEEP SEA FISHERMEN ABERDEEN

The National Mission to Deep Sea Fishermen, on the south side of Palmerston Road at its junction with South Market Street, was built in 1924 and designed by Pite, Son & Fairweather. It provided accommodation and support to fishermen in need. The Fishermen's Mission has cared for fishing communities since 1881 and is the only national maritime charity caring specifically for the needs of fishing communities throughout the UK. The Fishermen's Mission supports fishermen and their families in times of hardship, need, accident, illness or disaster at sea. Their mission statement is: "The Fishermen's Mission maintains a Christian presence in United Kingdom fishing ports, in order to provide, regardless of race or creed, spiritual support to fishermen, their families and those connected with the fishing industry". This building is now a hotel.

ABERDEEN HARBOUR FROM DOCK GATES. 677. G.W.W.

A late 19th century view of the harbour with the training ship *HMS Clyde* prominent in the centre of the picture. She was launched in 1828 and was moored in the Upper Dock where she served as a training ship for the Royal Naval Reserve. On the right of the picture is steam tug *Bon Accord*, with the Sugar House, where sugar was processed, on the quay behind.

ABERDEEN HARBOUR.

0108.

This picture, taken in 1905, shows the second *HMS Clyde* (formerly named the *Wild Swan*) to be moored in Aberdeen Harbour and used as a drill ship. This vessel was built in 1904 to replace the previous *HMS Clyde*. The *Alexander Pirie* is the steam schooner moored to the right of the picture. It was built in Aberdeen by A.Hall & Co in 1873. The Aberdeen skyline shows very clearly, with St Nicholas Church, the Town House, the Tolbooth, Mitchell Tower of Marischal College and the Salvation Army Citadel.

An early 1900s view of the harbour with timber being unloaded in the foreground. The timber is likely to have been shipped from Scandinavia, unloaded into the water and floated to the quays for distribution. *HMS Clyde* is just visible centre, having now been altered considerably for her duties as a drill ship.

A late 1940s view of Victoria Dock taken from Blaikie's Quay with the Regent (swing) Bridge to the left of the picture. When the bridge opened, ships could pass through to the Upper Dock. The skyline shows from the left St Nicholas Kirk steeple, the Harbour Office clock tower, the Town House clock tower, the Tolbooth Steeple (almost hidden by a crane) and the Mitchell Tower. In the centre of the picture at the bottom of Marischal Street is an impressive building, built as the Town and County Bank in 1901 of polished ashlar granite, to the design of Robert Gordon Wilson.

In the harbour is the Fishery Protection vessel *Brenda*. The *Brenda* was the first purpose-built Fishery Protection Vessel and was built by J. Reid of Glasgow in 1898. She served as an examination vessel with the Royal Navy in both world wars, and was withdrawn and broken up in 1951.

"TOILERS OF THE DEEP", ABERDEEN.

02178

Steam herring drifters at Aberdeen in the early 1900s. The herring fleet moved round the coast of Britain during the herring season and most vessels here were visitors to the port; they were registered in Banff. They may be the Bruce family's drifters, BF144 *Gaveny Brae* and BF195 *Inverboyndie*. To the far left is an Aberdeen registered drifter.

These are two of the Aberdeen Harbour steam tugs; the *St. Machar* and the *St. Fotin*. The *St. Machar* was built for the Ardrossan Harbour Company in 1898 by A Rodger of Port Glasgow and after serving with Liverpool owners between 1915 and in 1922 as the *Egad* it became the property of the Aberdeen Steam Tug Company. The *St. Fotin* was built by Dundee Shipbuilders in 1902 for Mersey owners and came to Aberdeen in 1932. The large boat in the background is the *SS St Sunniva*, one of the first purpose-built cruise ships. SS *St. Sunniva* was ordered by the North of Scotland, Orkney & Shetland Steam Navigation Company after the success of their earlier cruise vessel, the *St. Rognvald*. She was ordered from Hall, Russell & Company of Aberdeen for delivery in time for the 1887 season. Designed to resemble a classic steam yacht in form she carried a small steam launch for landing passengers when necessary. The *St. Sunniva* was a great commercial success as a cruise ship, but in 1908, she was converted into a ferry. Following this remodelling, the *St. Sunniva* entered service as a mail steamer on the Lerwick route, operating a weekly service from Leith and Aberdeen. She remained on this demanding service until 10th April 1930 when, while sailing north in fog, she ran aground on the uninhabited island of Mousa, off Shetland. All passengers and crew were rescued but the ship was a complete loss.

This pre First World War view shows the inner harbour with a collier being unloaded. The coal was first loaded into tubs, which were then hoisted onto the deck using the ship's derricks and windlass. The coal was then bagged to be carted away by the merchants. The collier is most likely the first *Thrift*, built in 1904 by Hall Russell for the Northern Co-operative Society.

Regent Quay around 1900 with a Norwegian wooden hulled steamer tied up alongside.

A view looking into Aberdeen Harbour showing the coaling stage centre where trawlers were bunkered in the days of coal-fired boilers. By the 1950s many vessels had been converted to burn oil. Unloading at the coal wharves is Ellis & McHardy's *Spray* of 1932. By this time the coal was discharged by grab, either using the ship's own derricks or the cranes seen in the picture.

This picture was taken between 1900 and 1910 and shows a busy morning on Regent Quay. Regent House at number 36 was built as a commercial property from grey granite ashlar in 1898 and designed by Alexander Marshall Mackenzie. The Custom House at number 35 was built in 1771 and is an excellent example of a Georgian Town House. It was originally a private mansion house belonging to James Gordon of Cobairdy. It became the official Aberdeen Custom House around 1892 and remained the property of HM Revenue and Customs until 2006. The building at an angle is at the bottom of Marischal Street. It was built in 1901 for the Aberdeen Town and County Bank and was designed in neo classical style by Robert Gordon Wilson, a prominent Aberdeen architect. The round building on the opposite corner is 60-62 Marischal Street, built between 1789 and 1821 as a commercial and residential building, forming a neat corner to the lower end of Marischal Street. A little further along is the clock tower on the Harbour Offices. The Harbour Offices at 14, 15 and 16 Regent Quay were built on the site of the old Weigh House. The building was designed by A. Marshall Mackenzie and built between 1883 and 1885 for Aberdeen Harbour Board. These five buildings are now all listed, category B, in a Group Category A. Next to the Harbour Offices is Weigh House Square, the site of several warehouses, which were owned by the Shore Porters Society and William Sanderson Wine Merchants and let out to tea merchants and distillers.

One of Britain's oldest companies, The Shore Porters Society (established in 1498), was created in Aberdeen to organise overland transportation of the goods that came into the harbour. It started when a group of porters (then called pynours) decided to form what we would now call a co-operative sometime prior to 1498. In that year, the city council granted them the right to carry sea-borne goods within Aberdeen at fixed rates. From the Middle Ages, pynours would transport goods from the Quays at Aberdeen Harbour or from Fittie, where the larger ships docked, up to the centre of Aberdeen. Especially in Victorian times, the Shore Porters also officiated at funerals, as bearers of coffins. Shore Porters is still a thriving removals, haulage and storage business. Nowadays, however, the handcart has given way to lorries!

Trinity Quay leading into Regent Quay. The weighbridge is in the bottom left corner and the harbour is busy with coal boats, coal merchants' huts, and horses and carts waiting to carry coal. The Harbour Office is the building with the arched fronts and clock tower. In the early 1900s Regent Quay was a busy commercial area, with banks, the Custom House, hotel, cooperages, ships' chandlers, the offices of the Marine Board, storage companies and shipping company offices including the Aberdeen Newcastle and Hull Steam Company.

The *SS Emma Hammar* was a Norwegian steamer built in 1902 for general cargo, later renamed *SS Kristine*. During the First World War while on a convoy from Skien to Leith carrying wood pulp, she was sunk on 16th October 1917 by the German warships *Bremse* and *Brummer* with the loss of eleven lives.

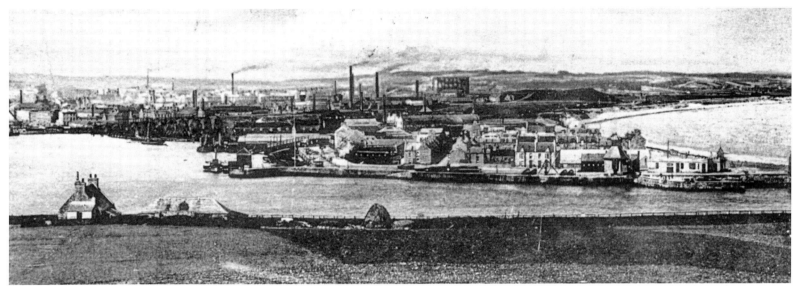

*Above*: The entrance to Aberdeen Harbour with the village of Fittie on the northside of the harbour and a very smoky Aberdeen beyond in the early 1900s. Aberdeen Bay and beach are on the right of the picture and agricultural land of Balnagask is in the foreground. The buildings on Pocra Quay include harbour master and pilot houses, the harbour' masters offices (The Roundhouse), and a customs house.

*Right*: "Fifies" leaving port. The Fifie was a traditional type of sailing boat, developed in the east of Scotland and used by Scottish fishermen from the 1850s until well into the 20th century mainly to fish for herring using drift nets. They had vertical stems and sterns, long straight keels, and wide beams, making them very stable in the water. The long keels made them difficult to manoeuvre in small harbours, but ideal for Aberdeen!

The slipway at Pocra Quay with Abercrombie Jetty (or "The Horseshoe") also showing below the Roundhouse, and a steam drifter leaving the harbour. The Roundhouse stands on the North Breakwater and was built circa 1798 as the Harbour Master's Station. It was later renamed the Navigation Control Centre. Harbour traffic was originally controlled by a signal involving three black balls mounted on a mast on the roof. In 1966 this signal was removed when the roof was raised to incorporate the new control tower and, in 1974, a sweeping radar antenna was placed on the roof to monitor ship movements. The Roundhouse became redundant in 2006 when the new Marine Operations Centre opened nearby but the building was later refurbished as office accommodation.

The large villas on the left were built just after 1900, the nearer one for the Assistant Harbour Master. Other houses were homes to the harbour pilots, fishermen and coopers. This picture was taken in the 1950s. To the south of the harbour mouth is Torry Point Battery which was built in 1859-61 to replace older buildings. The battery was built to defend the city and harbour from attack from the North Sea, and housed guns and soldiers. In 1895 it was partly dismantled but continued to be used for volunteer training. The valuation rolls for 1895-6 show six houses on the site, all occupied by gunners. The battery was occupied during both world wars and was also used as temporary accommodation when there was a shortage of houses in the city, but eventually fell into disrepair in 1950s.

Aberdeen Gas Works operated its own fleet of locomotives to carry coal to the gas works. Number 3, an 0-4-0 tank engine built by Andrew Barclay of Kilmarnock in 1926 is now preserved at the Grampian Transport Museum at Alford. Another engine from the fleet can be seen at Seaton Park where it is enjoyed by children in the play area!

An early post-war view of Class Z4 LNER ex Great North of Scotland Railway Manning Wardle 0-4-2 tank engine built in 1915 for service at Aberdeen Harbour when the Trustees permitted locomotive rather than horse haulage of wagons on the docks. It is seen on Blaikies Quay with one of Aberdeen's tugs and another unidentified vessel which had probably just come over from overhaul at Hall Russell's Shipyard.

Now in post 1948 British Railways livery 68190, a Z4 class 0-4-2 tank engine, awaits its next duty on Waterloo Quay. This engine had a short wheelbase essential for operating on the tightly curving dock lines.

Engine number 8193 with a train of empty wagons on the north side of the harbour at the foot of Marischal Street (where a bomb made a crater in the "cassies" or granite setts in July 1941). The railway lines crossing the bottom of the photograph are leading to the Regent Swing Bridge and over to Blaikies Quay.

To the right is the Town and County Bank building, designed by Robert Gordon Wilson in 1901 with an entrance onto Regent Quay but with the majority of the bank on Marischal Street. The Town and County Bank was amalgamated with the North of Scotland Bank in 1907 as can be seen from the lettering on the facade, but this photograph dates from the 1950s. This is a view looking up Marischal Street, with the clock tower of the Town House at the far end. In olden times, ne'er-do-wells were threatened with 'you'll die looking down Marischal Street'. The gibbet was in the Castlegate near the top of Marischal Street!

This photograph shows the railway goods line that ran from Waterloo Goods Station on Waterloo Quay at the harbour to Kittybrewster. The north-east of Scotland was known for growing oats and there were several large oatmeal mills in Aberdeen. One of the larger ones, the City Grain Mill is in the background with its square box on top of the roof. It was constructed in 1875 by Messrs Sutherland and Co. After many years as a flourmill and granary, it was purchased by the Shore Porters Society. The building was demolished in 2012.

To the right is Cotton Street. The houses that can be seen there were occupied by a variety of the town's people including a midwife, a grocer and a hairdresser. At one time, the town's gas works were situated in Cotton Street as were the Shore Porters Society's stables.

A busy day on Provost Blaikie's Quay, with the Roundhouse on Pocra Quay in the distance. Provost Blaikie's Quay and its neighbour Commercial Quay were created by the diversion of the River Dee in the 1860s, Commercial Quay becoming the home of Aberdeen Fish Market. The picture shows many fishing boats tied up alongside the quay to unload their catch. Individuals and merchants are buying fish. Barrels were used for storing fresh water on the fishing boats, and Torry was the home of several coopers. At the turn of the century Blaikie's Quay, along with Jamieson's Quay was also the home of timber merchants, coal merchants, stone merchants, slate merchants and the Aberdeen Lime Company. At the far end of Blaikie's and Commercial Quay is Matthew's Quay, which was once the wharf for the North of Scotland, Orkney and Shetland Steam Navigation Company.

**Fish Market, Aberdeen.**

The Fish Market on Commercial Quay. The covered market was built in 1889. Steam trawling for white fish was introduced into Aberdeen in 1882, so this large more modern market was required to accommodate a fleet of several hundred boats.

These two worthies are seen out getting a fry (enough fish for a meal) at the Fish Market on Commercial Quay. They are wearing ample heavy cotton skirts (probably with multiple flannel petticoats). The woman on the left of the photograph is wearing a cotton apron and a hand worked shawl that has seen better days. The woman on the right is wearing stout leather shoes, hand knitted stockings, man's jacket and a cap. Both women are warmly clad to keep out the cold on a winter's morning.

The fish box is labelled Irvin. Richard Irvin and Sons were one of the many companies to be established in Aberdeen, first as a trawling company, then becoming involved in the drifting for herring.

An early 1900s panorama of Aberdeen from the south, viewed from Torry. The river Dee runs across the middle of the picture with rowing boats pulled up on its banks. Running parallel to the Dee are a row of Fish Smoke Kilns or "Killees". St Nicholas Church, the Town House, Marischal College and the Salvation Army Citadel can all be seen on the horizon.

Fishing boats leave the harbour, with Paddy's Pier or the "Banana Pier" in the foreground.

A picture, taken just before the First World War, of six Torry Fish Workers.

An elderly fisherman redds the lines hooking them onto the sides of a basket. When a line fisherman returned from a trip, he had to clean the lines and hooks of seaweed and old bait, untangle the lines and fix new bait to each hook.

Skipper William Main from Torry was a line and then trawl skipper and after the First World War sailed as coaster skipper of the *M/V Rubislaw* sailing from Aberdeen to Germany.

Opposite: The *Craigievar* was one of five 73 foot trawlers built by the Fairmile shipyard of Berwick in 1959 for George Robb and Sons Ltd, trawl owners and fish salesmen of Commercial Quay. It was registered at Aberdeen as A304. The *Craigievar* crew are all from one family as far as we know and include George Main, Bill Main, Jock Main, Joseph Main (Sen), and Partin's Alex. Joseph was a half owner of the vessel.

*Right*: This is a small scale family operation with two generations of fishwives gutting fish. On the wall of the house is a wooden frame for air drying fish.

The *S.S. Aberdonian* was built by D. & W. Henderson of Glasgow for the Aberdeen Steam Navigation Co. Ltd. in 1909 for their Aberdeen to London service. Short sea voyages had become popular with the public from the 1890s and the *Aberdonian* could carry 100 First Class and 200 Second Class passengers. The *Aberdonian* became a hospital ship during the First World War and a depot ship for Motor Torpedo Boats during the Second World War. She was sold to Hong Kong owners in 1946, and was broken up in 1950 possibly after typhoon damage in 1948.

Wreck of the S.S. "G. Koch" off Girdleness, Aberdeen    "Adelphi Series"

Over the years, many ships came to grief on rocks along the coast near Aberdeen. The *S.S. G Koch* was a Danish cargo steamer built in 1888 by Turnbull Thomas & Sons of Whitby for Baxter H & Co. of Hull as the *Excelsior*. She was sold to Svendsen & Christensen of Copenhagen in 1902 and renamed. On 12th January 1913 the *G.Koch* was sailing from Odense in Denmark, bound for Burntisland in Fife with a deck cargo of pit props for the Fife coalfields and carrying water as ballast. In a south easterly storm, she went aground on the rocks below Girdleness Lighthouse. The ship was recognised as in distress and the Cove Lifesaving Apparatus was summoned. Seven crewmen were lost in trying to reach the shore and the ship was a total constructive loss.

October 1910 saw the launch of the *S.S. Intaba*, a passenger and cargo steamer, built by Hall Russell, which was at that time the largest vessel to be built in Aberdeen. The *Intaba* was of 4,382 tons gross and sailed under two other names, the *Waitomo* and the *Englestan*, being finally scrapped in Belgium in 1953. The paddle tug is the *John McConnochie* (1876) operated by John Newton & Son towage.

ABERDEEN HARBOUR

D 7780

A 1950s view of the inner harbour with the coastal tanker *Esso Dakotah* berthed. The *Esso Dakotah* was built by the Grangemouth Dockyard Co. in 1942 as the *Empire Gawain* for war service and was bought by Esso in 1946. She was scrapped in Belgium in 1962. By this date oil fuel had superseded coal on most of the fishing fleet and vessels such as this plied the harbours of the north east coast replenishing storage facilities. The vessel is 'light', sitting high in the water as her cargo has been discharged.

Situated near Torry, at the mouth of the River Dee, Girdleness Lighthouse was designed by Robert Louis Stevenson (grandfather to the author of the same name who wrote Treasure Island, Kidnapped and other novels) and built by James Gibb in 1833. The area beneath the lighthouse is known as Greyhope Bay. On April 1st 1813 a whaling ship called Oscar foundered in the bay. It had a crew of 43 but sadly only three crew members survived. This prompted the building of the lighthouse in this area. There had been many such wrecks in this area, but none with such a high loss of life. Girdleness Lighthouse was automated in 1991 and still remains a navigation aid for the many ships entering Aberdeen Harbour. It is now a listed building.

Girdleness Park, the plot of land adjacent to the lighthouse was purchased in May 1901, following public pressure for a formal park. The park was once well laid out and it was hoped that it would be one of the finest parks in Scotland, but the area today no longer has these features and its name has changed to Walker Park.

The Bay of Nigg in the 1920s with Girdleness Lighthouse on the skyline. The bay was for decades a very popular place of recreation for families from Torry and Aberdeen. Judging from shadows, the sun was shining when this picture was taken, but folk were wearing hats and coats! Some industries were also based at Nigg Bay; granite quarrying, kelp processing, salt production and in 1899 the Fishery Board for Scotland established a marine laboratory there. Its work continues today at another site in Torry. The tradition of people from Aberdeen visiting the Torry area for leisure had a long history. It may stretch back to the 17th century but was still very much in evidence in the early 20th century. Many families would make day trips to the Bay of Nigg. By the middle of the 20th century this age-old practice was in decline.

# The Three Musketeers

# OXFORD
UNIVERSITY PRESS

Great Clarendon Street, Oxford OX2 6DP

Oxford University Press is a department of the University of Oxford.
It furthers the University's objective of excellence in research, scholarship,
and education by publishing worldwide in

Oxford New York

Auckland Cape Town Dar es Salaam Hong Kong Karachi
Kuala Lumpur Madrid Melbourne Mexico City Nairobi
New Delhi Shanghai Taipei Toronto

With offices in

Argentina Austria Brazil Chile Czech Republic France Greece
Guatemala Hungary Italy Japan Poland Portugal Singapore
South Korea Switzerland Thailand Turkey Ukraine Vietnam

OXFORD and OXFORD ENGLISH are registered trade marks of
Oxford University Press in the UK and in certain other countries

ACKNOWLEDGEMENTS

*Illustrations by*: David A. Roach

*The publisher would like to thank the following for permission to reproduce photographs*: AKG-Images p59 (Execution of Charles I
/ Luyken); Bridgeman Images ppiv (Joan of Arc (c.1412-31), Gilbert, Sir John (1817-97)/Trustees of the Royal Watercolour
Society, London, UK), iv (Portrait of William Shakespeare (1564-1616) c.1610, Taylor, John (d.1651)/National Portrait
Gallery, London, UK), iv (Portrait of Cardinal de Richelieu (1585-1642), Champaigne, Philippe de (1602-74)/Musee des
Beaux-Arts, Rouen, France), iv (Louis XIII (1601-43), Champaigne, Philippe de (1602-74)/Prado, Madrid, Spain), iv (Anne
of Austria (1601-66) with her son Louis XIV (1638-1715), French School, (17th century)/Chateau de Versailles, France), iv
(Portrait of King Charles I (1600-49), Dyck, Sir Anthony van (1599-1641)/Private Collection/Philip Mould Ltd, London), 58
(Portrait of Charles I (1600-49), Dyck, Sir Anthony van (1599-1641)/Private Collection), 58 (Portrait of Oliver Cromwell
(1599-1658) 1649, Walker, Robert (1607-60)/Leeds Museums and Galleries (Leeds Art Gallery) U.K.), 58 (Portrait of Nell
Gwynne, c.1680, Lely, Sir Peter (1618-80)/Geffrye Museum, London, UK), 58 (Portrait of King Charles II (1630-85), c.1675,
Lely, Sir Peter (1618-80)/Private Collection/Philip Mould Ltd, London), 59 (The Dashing Cavalier, Lomax, John Arthur
(1857-1923)/Haynes Fine Art at the Bindery Galleries, Broadway), 59 (Puritan, Roundhead, Pettie, John (1839-93)/Sheffield
Galleries and Museums Trust, UK/Museums Sheffield), 59 (John Milton, Faithorne, William (1616-91)/Huntington Library
and Art Gallery, San Marino, CA, USA/The Huntington Library, Art Collections & Botanical Gardens), 59 (Self Portrait with
a Sunflower, after 1632, Dyck, Sir Anthony van (1599-1641)/Private Collection/Philip Mould Ltd, London).

*Cover*: Ilian Stage courtesy of Alamy Images

**DOMINOES**

Series Editors: Bill Bowler and Sue Parminter

# The Three Musketeers

*Alexandre Dumas*

Text adaptation by Clare West

Illustrated by David A. Roach

Alexandre Dumas was born near Paris in 1802. His grandmother was a Haitian slave, and his father, a general in the French army, died when Alexandre was only four. As a child, Dumas was poor, and had little education, but when he was twenty he went to live in Paris and soon became successful both as a playwright and a novelist. His most famous books, *The Three Musketeers* (1844) and *The Count of Monte Cristo* (1845) are both available in the Dominoes series. Alexandre Dumas died in 1870. His son, also called Alexandre, was a successful novelist, too.

OXFORD
UNIVERSITY PRESS

## BEFORE READING

**1** The story happens in the seventeenth century. Which people are you going to read about? Tick the boxes.

**a** ☐

*Joan of Arc*
FRENCH LEADER

**b** ☐

*William Shakespeare*
ENGLISH WRITER

**c** ☐

*Cardinal Richelieu*
PRIME MINISTER OF FRANCE

**d** ☐

*Louis XIII*
KING OF FRANCE

**e** ☐

*Anne of Austria*
KING LOUIS XIII'S WIFE AND QUEEN OF FRANCE

**f** ☐

*Charles I*
KING OF ENGLAND

**2** Which of these things do you think you will read about? Tick the boxes.

**a** ☐ Men and women falling in love.

**b** ☐ People fighting.

**c** ☐ People sailing to America.

**d** ☐ People escaping from prison.

# Chapter 1

## D'Artagnan meets the three musketeers

The **Captain** of the King's **musketeers**, **Monsieur** de Tréville, sat back in his chair and looked with interest at the young man in front of him. 'So you're the son of my old friend **d'Artagnan**!' he said. 'Now tell me, why have you left your village to come all the way to Paris?'

'I'm hoping to become one of the King's musketeers, **sir**,' said d'Artagnan. 'If a great man like you can help me—'

'I see a lot of young men like you, who want to become musketeers. It isn't easy. You have to show how **brave** you are. It's strange that you haven't brought a letter with you, from your father—'

'Sir, I had one, but a man stole it from me, when I stopped for some food at the town of **Meung**! A dark, well-dressed man.' Just then d'Artagnan gave a shout. 'Look, sir, there he is, outside your window! Excuse me, I must catch him!' And he ran out of the room.

De Tréville smiled and shook his head. 'What a wild young man! He'll be a good musketeer one day!'

On his way downstairs d'Artagnan **bumped into** a tall, good-looking musketeer. 'Sorry!' he cried, and ran on.

But the musketeer stopped him. 'You must say more than "Sorry" if you bump into me. I'm Athos, and I don't like your **behaviour**. Have you just arrived from the country?'

'What do you mean?' replied d'Artagnan. 'I *am* from the country, but I'm as good as you are!'

'We'll see about that,' said Athos. 'I'll fight you at twelve o'clock outside the church over there.'

'Right,' said d'Artagnan. 'I'll be there, don't worry,' and he ran off again, hoping to find the man from Meung. In

**captain** the leader of a group of soldiers

**musketeer** a soldier who fights with swords and guns

**Monsieur** /mə'sjɜː/ Mr

**d'Artagnan** /dɑː'tænjɒn/

**sir** you say this when you talk to a rich or important man

**brave** not afraid of doing dangerous things

**Meung** /mɜːŋ/

**bump into** to hit someone with your body when you are walking or running

**behaviour** the way that you do and say things

1

*'I'll be there!'* his hurry he bumped into a second musketeer, called Porthos, and knocked his hat onto the ground. It was a fine, expensive hat, and Porthos was very angry.

'I'll teach you a lesson, young man!' he shouted. 'Meet me on the bridge at one o'clock! And bring your **sword**!'

'I'll be there!' d'Artagnan called back. Just then he saw a third musketeer in front of him, and a **lady's glove** on the ground at his feet. Without thinking he ran over and gave the glove to the musketeer.

'Does it belong to a friend, perhaps?' he asked, smiling.

'That's none of your business!' replied the musketeer angrily. 'I'll have to fight you for that! Meet me outside the theatre at two o'clock. My name's Aramis.'

Now d'Artagnan couldn't see the man from Meung anywhere, and he had to fight three musketeers, the bravest and best fighters in the country. But luckily for him, when

**sword** a long, sharp knife for fighting

**lady** a woman from a good family

**glove** a thing that you wear on your hand

Athos, Porthos, and Aramis heard that they were all fighting the same man, they decided to forget his behaviour. They saw how brave he was, and he soon became their friend. They even found a **servant**, called **Planchet**, for him.

⁂

A few days later, Planchet showed a visitor into d'Artagnan's room. It was **Bonacieux**, the **owner** of the house. He was looking very worried. 'Sir,' he cried, 'please help me! I don't know what to do! Yesterday someone **kidnapped** my wife!'

'Really?' said d'Artagnan, interested. 'Tell me more.'

'Well, she goes to the **palace** every day, because she works for the Queen. It was a dark, well-dressed man who kidnapped her—'

'Aha!' cried d'Artagnan. 'That sounds like the man from Meung! Go on.'

'You see, my wife knows all the Queen's secrets. She knows that very soon an important Englishman will visit the Queen – you won't tell anyone this, will you? – perhaps you know who it is—'

'The **Duke** of Buckingham?' asked d'Artagnan. Most people in Paris knew that Buckingham was in love with the French Queen.

'Shh! The walls have ears! Yes. And the **Cardinal**, the King's first **minister**, wants to show the King that his wife has a lover! So he sent one of his men to kidnap my wife and find out what she knows!'

'Leave it to me,' said d'Artagnan. 'I'll find your wife for you.'

⁂

Later d'Artagnan told the three musketeers about the kidnapping.

'Remember that the Cardinal's our enemy and that we must keep the Queen out of danger,' said Porthos.

'We'll be stronger than the Cardinal if we work together,'

**servant** a person who works for someone rich

**Planchet** /ˈplɒnʃeɪ/

**Bonacieux** /bɒnˈæsjə/

**owner** the person that something belongs to

**kidnap** to take someone away and keep them as a prisoner

**palace** a big house where a king lives

**duke** a very important man

**cardinal** a very important man in the Catholic church

**minister** an important person who helps the king

said d'Artagnan. 'One for all, and all for one!' They shook hands on it.

⁂

That evening d'Artagnan was in his room upstairs, when he heard a woman hurrying down the street. He looked out of the window. 'Perhaps it's **Madame** Bonacieux,' he thought, 'and she's escaped!' She went into the house, and at once started screaming.

'She's in trouble!' d'Artagnan told himself. He ran downstairs and knocked down the front door. Inside there were three soldiers, holding the young woman a prisoner. It wasn't long before the three were running away, afraid of d'Artagnan's angry shouts and his heavy sword.

Now d'Artagnan was alone with Madame Bonacieux. He saw her beautiful face, and for the first time he knew that he was in love.

*He knew that he was in love.*

'Sir, thank you for what you've done!' she said warmly.

'It was nothing, Madame. Those men work for the Cardinal. They wanted to kidnap you again, I think. They want to know about the Queen's secrets. You're in danger here.'

'Where can I go? There's a plan – I need to be free—'

'I can take you to the house of my friend Athos. He's away tonight, so you'll be alone, and nobody will know you're there.'

'Then please, let's go there now.' She took his arm, and together they went to Athos's house, where d'Artagnan left her.

But later that night Madame Bonacieux went out. She walked quickly to a house in the next street, where the Duke of Buckingham was waiting for her. She took him through a secret door into the palace. The Queen came to meet them, looking more beautiful than ever. Buckingham could not stop himself from **kissing** her feet.

'Sir!' said the Queen. 'We cannot speak for long!'

'But how happy I am to see you, even if only for a moment!' said Buckingham.

'I must tell you now that we can never see each other again. There will be **war** between our two countries, and – and I am married!'

'But love is greater than that! For three long years I've loved you, I've thought of you and hoped that you loved me too!'

'I cannot give you any hope,' said the Queen, looking away. 'Go, sir! If they find you here, you will die! And I'll be very unhappy!'

'You do love me after all! Give me something to keep, something which belongs to you, and I'll go at once!'

'Very well, then. Take these **diamonds**, and think of me.' She gave him a small **wooden** box, and he kissed her hand many times.

'I'll see you again, my Queen!' he cried, leaving the room.

**kiss** to touch lovingly with your mouth

**war** fighting between countries and people

**diamond** a very expensive stone that usually has no colour

**wooden** made of wood

## READING CHECK

**Are these sentences true or false? Tick the boxes.**

| | | True | False |
|---|---|---|---|
| **a** | D'Artagnan wants to work for the Cardinal. | ☐ | ☑ |
| **b** | D'Artagnan nearly fights with Athos, Porthos and Aramis. | ☐ | ☐ |
| **c** | Athos, Porthos and Aramis are soon d'Artagnan's friends. | ☐ | ☐ |
| **d** | Someone took Monsieur Bonacieux's daughter from his house. | ☐ | ☐ |
| **e** | D'Artagnan helps Madame Bonacieux. | ☐ | ☐ |
| **f** | Later Madame Bonacieux takes the Duke of Buckingham to meet the King of France. | ☐ | ☐ |
| **g** | The Queen gives the Duke her diamonds. | ☐ | ☐ |

## WORD WORK

**1 Match the words in the hat with the pictures.**

kiss
sword
gloves palace
cardinal diamond

a .palace.........

b .................

c .....................

d .....................

e .............

f .....................

**2** **Use the letters in the gloves to complete these sentences about the story.**

**a** Athos, Porthos and Aramis are m u s k e t e e r s.

*sukreete*

**b** D'Artagnan is very b _ _ _ _ _. He isn't afraid of fighting three musketeers.

*erav*

**c** When d'Artagnan b _ _ _ _ _ _ _ _ Athos, Athos is angry.

*sump onti*

**d** Monsieur de Tréville is the c _ _ _ _ _ _ _ of the king's soldiers.

*nitapa*

**e** The musketeers are very good at fighting with s _ _ _ _ _ _.

*sdwro*

**f** Planchet is d'Artagnan's s _ _ _ _ _ _ _.

*tanver*

**g** The Cardinal is the King of France's first m _ _ _ _ _ _ _ _.

*tenisir*

**h** Someone has k _ _ _ _ _ _ _ _ _ Mme Bonacieux.

*pandipde*

**i** The Queen gives a w _ _ _ _ _ box to Buckingham.

*edono*

**j** Porthos is the o _ _ _ _ of a fine hat.

*ernw*

## GUESS WHAT

**What happens in the next chapter? Tick four boxes.**

**a** ☐ We learn more about Monsieur Bonacieux.

**b** ☐ We learn more about the Cardinal's plans.

**c** ☐ D'Artagnan helps the Queen of France.

**d** ☐ D'Artagnan helps the King of France.

**e** ☐ D'Artagnan helps the King of England.

**f** ☐ D'Artagnan helps the Cardinal.

**g** ☐ The three musketeers arrive in England.

**h** ☐ Buckingham loses some of the diamonds.

# Chapter 2 Diamonds for the Queen

*M*adame Bonacieux was too busy worrying about the Queen's secret to think about her husband. While Buckingham was kissing the Queen's hand, Monsieur Bonacieux was standing in front of the Cardinal. The little man was white and shaking. He knew that the Cardinal was as **powerful** as the King. 'He'll kill me if he wants to, and no one can stop him! Oh, why did I marry my wife? She's got me into all this trouble!' he thought.

But luckily, the great Cardinal wasn't angry with him at all. After a few questions about Madame Bonacieux, he said, 'My dear monsieur, I'm so sorry that my men had to bring you here. But we've had a most interesting talk. Perhaps you'll help me if I need you another time. Please take this bag of gold, and feel free to leave.'

Bonacieux loved money nearly as much as he loved himself. 'Oh sir!' he cried. 'Thank you, thank you, sir!' And when he was out of the room, he shouted as loudly as possible, 'Long live the Cardinal!'

The next day the Cardinal heard about the Queen's secret visitor from one of the palace servants. First he went to see the King. Then he called another person to his office. She was a beautiful, well-dressed woman, with long **blonde** hair and large blue eyes. It was Lady de Winter.

'Milady, do you remember the King giving the Queen twelve diamonds for her birthday? Well, now she's given them to her lover!'

Milady smiled coldly. 'How stupid of her!' she said.

'You must leave for England today. The Duke of Buckingham will want to wear the diamonds, I'm sure. So

**powerful** rich and important

**blonde** light yellow

8

you must get near him, at a dance perhaps, and steal two of the diamonds. Bring them back to me, and then we can show them to the King.'

'Leave it to me,' said Milady.

At the palace the Queen was speaking worriedly to Madame Bonacieux. 'The King's just told me that there'll be an important dinner in a week's time. He wants me to wear my diamonds, but I gave them to Buckingham! The Cardinal visited the King this morning – it's part of his plan to show the King that I have a lover! What can I do?'

'We must get those diamonds back at once, Madame. Don't worry, I know someone who will help us. Write a letter to the Duke of Buckingham, and give it to me. My friend will take it to London.'

Madame Bonacieux was thinking of that good-looking young man, d'Artagnan. 'He's very brave!' she thought. And when she told d'Artagnan about the Queen's letter, he was more than pleased to help. He loved Madame Bonacieux, and he loved his Queen.

*'What can I do?'*

'Her secret is **safe** with me!' he cried.

The next day he called the three musketeers together.

'Friends, we must travel in secret to England,' he told them.

'Can't you tell us why?' asked Athos.

'The Queen needs our help. That's all I can say.'

'I'll buy a new sword for the journey,' said Porthos happily.

'There's no time for that,' said d'Artagnan, 'we leave at once. Now listen carefully. We'll ride together, and fight to the death if anyone **attacks** us. I'm sure that the Cardinal is going to send his men to stop us. I have a letter from the Queen in my pocket. If I die, the next man must take the letter and ride on. If he dies, the next man must take it, and so on. The letter must arrive safely in London.'

*The four friends and Planchet rode out of Paris.*

Half an hour later the four friends and Planchet rode out of Paris, their swords in their hands. They did not know that the Cardinal's men were following them. At Chantilly

three men attacked Porthos, and he had to stay there and fight them. At Beauvais someone shot Aramis from an upstairs window, and he was badly hurt and couldn't go on. Then at Amiens two men took Athos prisoner while he was asleep. 'That just leaves you and me, Planchet!' said d'Artagnan.

The two men sailed to England, bought new horses and rode to London. There they soon found the Duke of Buckingham's house. D'Artagnan asked to see the Duke, who took him into a **private** room at once.

'What have you come to tell me?' asked the Duke. 'You come from France. Has something happened to the Queen? Quickly!'

'She is well, sir,' answered d'Artagnan, 'but she is in great danger. She sends you a letter. Here it is.'

'A letter from the Queen!' Buckingham took it with shaking hands and read every word. He looked up at d'Artagnan. 'I must send back her diamonds with you. Here they are. I keep them with me at all times.' He took a wooden box out of his pocket and opened it. Suddenly he gave a cry. 'There are only ten diamonds! Two have gone!'

'Has someone stolen them, sir?' asked d'Artagnan.

'Yes, I remember now. I was wearing them last night, and I was dancing with Lady de Winter. She works for the Cardinal, I think. But don't worry, young man. My **jeweller** will make two more, which will look just like the others. Stay here tonight, and tomorrow I'll give you the box of twelve diamonds to take back to the Queen. Shake hands with me, d'Artagnan, you're a very brave man.'

And so the next day d'Artagnan and Planchet were on another ship, sailing back to France. On their way they had no more adventures, and they arrived safely home in the evening. That night d'Artagnan slept in his bed at Monsieur Bonacieux's house, with the Queen's diamonds in his hand.

**private** away from other people

**jeweller** a person who works with expensive stones

## READING CHECK

**1 Put these sentences in the correct order. Number them 1–10.**

**a** ☐ The Cardinal asks Milady to get two of the diamonds from Buckingham.

**b** ☐ The King asks the Queen to wear her diamonds to a dinner.

**c** ☐ D'Artagnan gives the Duke of Buckingham a letter about the diamonds.

**d** ☐ D'Artagnan takes the box of diamonds back to the Queen of France.

**e** ☐ The Duke finds two of the diamonds have gone from their box.

**f** ☐ The Cardinal questions Monsieur Bonacieux.

**g** ☐ Madame Bonacieux asks d'Artagnan to go to England.

**h** ☐ The Duke's jeweller makes two new diamonds to go in the box.

**i** ☐ The three musketeers help d'Artagnan leave France.

**j** ☐ The next day the Cardinal finds out about the Duke's visit to the Queen.

**2 Match the first and second parts of the sentences.**

**a** 'He's very brave,'

**b** 'How stupid of her,'

**c** 'She's got me into all this trouble,'

**d** 'Her secret is safe with me,'

**e** 'You must get near him,'

**f** 'He wants me to wear my diamonds,'

**1** says Milady about the Queen.

**2** says d'Artagnan about the Queen.

**3** says the Queen about the King.

**4** says Monsieur Bonacieux about his wife.

**5** thinks Madame Bonacieux about d'Artagnan.

**6** says the Cardinal to Milady.

## WORD WORK

**Use the words in the box of diamonds to complete the sentences on page 13.**

attack, blonde, jeweller, powerful, private, safe

**a** The Queen of France can only meet Buckingham in …*private*…

**b** The Cardinal is a very ……………… man.

**c** Buckingham thinks the Queen's diamonds are ……………… but he is wrong.

**d** Milady has blue eyes and ……………… hair.

**e** Buckingham pays his ……………… to make two new diamonds to go in the box.

**f** The Cardinal's men ……………… the musketeers.

## GUESS WHAT

**What happens in the next chapter? Tick three boxes.**

**a** ☐ D'Artagnan gives the diamonds to Madame Bonacieux.

**b** ☐ D'Artagnan gives the diamonds to Milady.

**c** ☐ The King is angry with the Queen.

**d** ☐ The Cardinal's men take the diamonds from Madame Bonacieux.

**e** ☐ The Queen wears the diamonds one evening at a party.

**f** ☐ The King is angry with the Cardinal.

# Chapter 3
## A second kidnapping

**V**ery early the next morning d'Artagnan went to the palace to find Madame Bonacieux. He gave her the small wooden box, and she hurried happily away to give it to the Queen.

That evening everybody in Paris was talking about the dinner at the palace. Hundreds of important people waited in the great dining room for the King and Queen to arrive. First came the King, richly dressed, but looking very angry. Next was the Cardinal, looking **proud** but worried. And last, the Queen, looking beautiful, but tired. The King and Cardinal were some way away from the Queen, so they couldn't see her very well. Both of them kept their eyes on her dress. She was wearing the diamonds, but it wasn't easy to count them.

'Are there ten or twelve?' the Cardinal asked himself. He was playing a dangerous **game**, and he knew it. 'I've told the King that two are **missing**. Milady's given me the two diamonds stolen from Buckingham. So how can there be twelve on the Queen's dress?'

Suddenly the King called across the long table to the Queen, 'I am sorry that you're not wearing all my diamonds, Madame.'

The Queen lifted her beautiful head proudly. 'I don't know what you mean, sir,' she said. And she turned to him. The King and the Cardinal counted twelve diamonds on her dress.

'Well, Cardinal,' shouted the King angrily, 'what's all this about? Are you laughing at me? Explain yourself at once!'

'I'm sorry, sir,' replied the Cardinal. 'I – I made a mistake.'

The Queen smiled secretly to herself. And so did

**proud** feeling that you are more important than other people

**game** a secret plan or way of playing with other people's feelings

**missing** not there

14

d'Artagnan. He was the only one in the crowd who knew what was happening.

Just then he felt a woman's hand on his arm. He looked down and saw a letter on the ground. The woman was moving away, but he knew that it was Madame Bonacieux. He took up the letter, opened it and read it. It said:

> I'd like to thank you for what you've done. Come to the little house at the end of Avenue **Saint Cloud** at ten o'clock tomorrow night, and wait outside for me.
>
> Constance Bonacieux

The next evening he rode excitedly through the dark streets to the Avenue Saint Cloud. It was a quiet and lonely part of Paris, and even brave d'Artagnan started to feel afraid. But he saw no one, and waited until eleven o'clock outside the little house. He began to feel worried. 'Why isn't she here?' he thought. 'What's happened?'

Then he saw an old man walking slowly past. 'Excuse me!' said d'Artagnan. 'Have you seen a young woman go into this house?'

The old man looked afraid. 'If I tell you, perhaps the Cardinal's men will find out, and kill me!'

'Oh, so his men were here, were they?'

'That's right, sir, with a dark, well-dressed man. They took the young woman from the house and drove away in a **carriage**.'

'This is terrible!' thought d'Artagnan. 'The man from Meung has kidnapped the poor woman again! Is she hurt? Is she dead? How can I get her back this time? I know! I'll ask Athos what to do.'

He rode fast to Athos's house and woke up his friend. Athos listened carefully to d'Artagnan's story.

**Saint Cloud**
/sæŋ kluː/

**carriage** an old kind of car that horses pull

'Too late to do anything tonight,' he said, 'but tomorrow I'll ask Monsieur de Tréville to speak to the Queen about it. She'll find out where the Cardinal is keeping Madame Bonacieux prisoner.'

'Thank you. You're lucky that you've never been in love!'

'Do you think so? But I can tell you a love story, if you like. It's about a friend of mine, not me, you understand. Well, my friend was the head of one of the great French families. When he was twenty-five, he **fell in love with** a girl of sixteen. She was very beautiful, with long blonde hair and blue eyes. He married her and for a time they were very happy. Then one day, when they were riding together, she fell off her horse and hurt her arm. He ran to help her, and opened the top of her dress for her. There, on her **shoulder**, he saw that she was **branded**!'

'What a terrible story!' cried d'Artagnan.

'She was branded because she was a thief. He killed her – he **hanged** her from the nearest tree. That's why I never fall in love now.'

D'Artagnan couldn't forget Athos's story. He was riding home, thinking hard, when he saw a carriage with a

beautiful blonde lady in it. She was talking angrily to a well-dressed Englishman. He was sitting on his horse and laughing at her.

'Can I help you, Madame?' called d'Artagnan. 'Is this **gentleman** being **rude** to you? I can teach him a lesson, if you like!'

Milady smiled up at d'Artagnan. 'Thank you, sir, but this gentleman is my **brother-in-law**, Lord de Winter.'

De Winter looked angry. 'This is none of your business, young man,' he said crossly. 'Kindly leave us alone!'

'No one speaks to me like that, sir,' replied d'Artagnan. 'Let's talk about this later, on the south side of the palace, perhaps?'

'Shall we say six o'clock? I'll be there,' said de Winter.

D'Artagnan's plan was to find out more about Milady. When, later that day, the two men met and fought, d'Artagnan won easily.

'I won't kill you,' he told de Winter, 'if you agree to take me to visit your **sister-in-law**. When I saw her today, I fell in love with her.'

Lord de Winter thanked d'Artagnan for **sparing** his life, and they agreed to meet at Milady's house the next day.

**gentleman** a man from a rich family who does not need to work

**rude** speaking loudly or crossly, using bad words

**brother-in-law** your wife's or husband's brother

**sister-in-law** your wife's or husband's sister

**spare** not to take

*'Can I help you, Madame?'*

## READING CHECK

**Match the first and second parts of these sentences.**

**a** D'Artagnan gives the box of diamonds . . .

**b** There is a party at the palace . . .

**c** The Cardinal says that the Queen . . .

**d** The Queen shows everyone . . .

**e** Madame Bonacieux asks d'Artagnan . . .

**f** The man from Meung kidnaps . . .

**g** D'Artagnan meets Milady . . .

**h** D'Artagnan and Lord de Winter . . .

**1** that she is wearing all twelve diamonds.

**2** is wearing only ten diamonds.

**3** to meet her one night.

**4** to Madame Bonacieux to take to the Queen.

**5** Madame Bonacieux again.

**6** for hundreds of important people.

**7** fight together.

**8** talking angrily with her brother-in-law.

## WORD WORK

**Correct the boxed words in these sentences. They all come from Chapter 3.**

**a** The Cardinal is a very **prowl** man. _proud_

**b** What a **rode** man. He's always talking and he never listens to other people. ................

**c** She killed lots of people and so when they caught her, they **handed** her from a tree. ................

**d** I hurt my **boulder** yesterday and now I can't move my arm very well. ................

**e** They got into an old **marriage** and drove off. ................

**f** Two of the diamonds are **kissing** from their box. ................

**g** Come on! Don't play **names** with me! ................

**h** Don't kill me. Please **spade** my life. ................

**i** She was **branched** on her arm. ................

## GUESS WHAT

**What happens in the next chapter? Tick the boxes.**

|  | Yes | Perhaps | No |
|---|---|---|---|

**a** D'Artagnan falls in love with Milady.

☐  ☐  ☐

**b** Milady falls in love with d'Artagnan.

☐  ☐  ☐

**c** Milady meets a secret lover.

☐  ☐  ☐

**d** D'Artagnan falls in love with Milady's servant.

☐  ☐  ☐

**e** Athos is worried about Milady.

☐  ☐  ☐

# Chapter 4  A dangerous woman

Milady was very kind to d'Artagnan when Lord de Winter took him to her house. The young man found her very beautiful, and he no longer thought so often of Constance Bonacieux. Every day for the next month he visited Milady. He began to think that she really liked him.

One day, when he arrived at her house, her **maid**, Kitty stopped him. She was a **pretty** girl, who always smiled at him.

'Can I speak to you in private, sir?' she asked.

'Of course, Kitty. What is it?'

'Come up to my room, sir, where no one can hear us.'

Together they went upstairs to her small bedroom. D'Artagnan looked around. 'Does that door open into Milady's room?' he asked.

'Yes, sir. You love Milady, don't you?' asked Kitty unhappily.

'Yes, Kitty, I'm wildly in love with her.'

'I'm sorry about that, sir, because Milady doesn't love you at all. Look at this letter.' And she gave d'Artagnan a letter to read. It said:

> *You haven't replied to me, Count.*
> *Don't you love me? I'm waiting for*
> *you. Come at ten o'clock any evening.*
> *Lady Clarice de Winter*

**maid** a woman who works in a rich person's house

**pretty** beautiful

**count** an important man

'Did Milady write this and ask you to take it to someone?' asked d'Artagnan.

'Yes, sir, the **Count** de Wardes. She's in love with him. I'm telling you this, sir, because – because I'm in love with you myself!'

'Aha!' thought d'Artagnan. 'Kitty's love for me will be useful. I can find out more about Milady from her.' He said nothing, but gave Kitty a kiss. They spent the evening talking, laughing, and kissing.

At midnight they heard Milady call 'Kitty!' from her bedroom. D'Artagnan jumped up and hid himself in a cupboard. Kitty ran into Milady's room, and d'Artagnan could hear their conversation.

'Monsieur d'Artagnan didn't visit you tonight, Milady.'

'He'll come tomorrow. I'm planning to **take my revenge** on him.'

'Don't you love him, Milady?'

'Love him? I hate him! Why didn't he kill Lord de Winter? When my brother-in-law dies, I shall have all his money!'

'And Madame Bonacieux? What happened to her?'

'Oh, her! She's just a woman from the back streets. The Cardinal and I are keeping her somewhere safe, don't worry.'

D'Artagnan was **horrified**. Milady, who looked so beautiful, was truly **evil**! He began planning to take his revenge on her.

The next day he visited Kitty and gave her a letter for Milady. It said:

> Lady de Winter, how lucky I am to win your love! I shall visit you this evening at ten o'clock.
> Count Robert de Wardes

'But you wrote this!' cried Kitty.

'Yes, and tonight I'll visit Milady at ten. It'll be dark in her room, and she'll think that I am the Count de Wardes. Perhaps then I can find out what has happened to my poor Constance.'

In the end Kitty agreed, and d'Artagnan's plan worked

**take your revenge** to hurt someone who has hurt you

**horrified** very surprised and afraid

**evil** very bad

well. He spent the evening with Milady, talking softly of love and kissing her beautiful face in the soft orange light that came from the fire. Before he left, Milady took his hand. 'Oh Count,' she said, 'I'm so happy that you love me! Take this ring, and then you'll never forget me!' She put a diamond ring on the young man's finger.

The next morning d'Artagnan went to see his friend Athos, and told him all about his visits to Kitty and Milady. But Athos was more interested in the ring. 'Where did you get this?' he asked.

'Beautiful, isn't it? It's a present from Milady.'

'That's strange,' thought Athos. 'It looks like a ring that belonged to me once. I gave it to the woman who loved me, I thought. How stupid I was!'

Athos didn't speak for a moment. 'You're my friend, d'Artagnan,' he said. 'Listen to me. Forget about Milady. I don't know her, but I know that she's evil and dangerous. Keep away from her.'

D'Artagnan knew that Athos was right, but it was difficult to think of never seeing Milady again. He visited her that evening.

'Milady, I saw the Count de Wardes today,' he said.

'The Count?' Milady's face changed colour. 'Did you? Er . . . what did he say? Did he . . . speak of me?'

'I'm sorry to say that he was showing everybody your ring. He was laughing at you. A true gentleman is never so rude to a lady!'

Milady was white and she was shaking. 'He – he laughed at me? Me! D'Artagnan, that man is now my enemy! Fight him for me!'

'I'll be happy to kill him for you, Milady!'

'If you do that, we can be happy together, you and I.' She smiled, and took his hand. She let him kiss her again and again.

D'Artagnan forgot Athos's words, and he forgot Constance. He thought that Milady loved him, and so he said, smiling, 'You know that it was really me here in your room last night!'

'What do you mean?' asked Milady, pulling away from him.

'It wasn't the Count de Wardes who came to visit you, it was me.'

'Is that true? You'll be sorry for playing games with me, young man!' And angrily she attacked him, pulling out his hair and hitting him hard. D'Artagnan held her away from him. Just then her dress fell off her shoulder, and he was horrified to see that she was branded!

'I'm going to kill you!' she screamed wildly, holding a knife in her hand. The young man ran downstairs and into the street.

*He was horrified to see that she was branded!*

## READING CHECK

**1 Are these sentences true or false? Tick the boxes.**

|   |   | True | False |
|---|---|------|-------|
| **a** | De Wardes gives Kitty a letter for Milady. | ☐ | ☑ |
| **b** | Milady knows at once that the Count de Wardes who visits her is really D'Artagnan. | ☐ | ☐ |
| **c** | Athos thinks that he has seen Milady's ring before. | ☐ | ☐ |
| **d** | Milady wants d'Artagnan to fight de Wardes. | ☐ | ☐ |
| **e** | At the end of the chapter, Milady loves d'Artagnan. | ☐ | ☐ |

**2 Correct nine more mistakes in the chapter summary.**

Constance Bonacieux
D'Artagnan forgets ~~the Queen~~ and goes to see Milady every day for a year. Milady has

a pretty maid called Kitty. Kitty tells D'Artagnan that Milady is in love with de Tréville.

Kitty herself is in love with Aramis. She shows him a letter from de Wardes. D'Artagnan

goes to visit Milady one morning saying that he is de Wardes. Milady gives him a gold

ring. Porthos is very interested in this ring. He tells d'Artagnan to be careful with

Milady. D'Artagnan tells Milady that he, and not de Wardes, visited her. Milady is very

happy with d'Artagnan. In the fight that they have, d'Artagnan sees that Milady's leg is

branded.

## WORD WORK

**Find words in the flowers to complete the sentences.**

**a** Kitty is Milady's
m a i d.

**b** She is a p _ _ _ _ _
young woman.

**c** Milady is an e _ _ _
woman who
smiles a lot.

**d** She is in love with
the C _ _ _ _
de Wardes.

**e** D'Artagnan is
h _ _ _ _ _ _ _ _
by Milady because
she is very bad,
but he is interested
in her too.

**f** Milady wants to take
her r _ _ _ _ _ _
on d'Artagnan
because he didn't
kill Lord de Winter.

## GUESS WHAT

**What happens in the next chapter? Tick the boxes.**

|  | Yes | No |
|---|---|---|
| **a** Athos learns that Milady was once his wife. | ☐ | ☐ |
| **b** The Cardinal wants to give d'Artagnan a job. | ☐ | ☐ |
| **c** D'Artagnan agrees to work for the Cardinal. | ☐ | ☐ |
| **d** D'Artagnan and the three musketeers go to fight the English. | ☐ | ☐ |
| **e** The Cardinal sends Milady to kill Buckingham. | ☐ | ☐ |
| **f** Milady wants to kill d'Artagnan. | ☐ | ☐ |
| **g** Athos speaks to Milady. | ☐ | ☐ |
| **h** Athos kills Milady. | ☐ | ☐ |

# Chapter 5

# Meetings
## with the Cardinal

D'Artagnan ran all the way through Paris without stopping. When he arrived at Athos's house, he ran at once into his friend's bedroom.

'What's happened?' cried Athos, sitting up in bed. 'Is the King dead? Or have you killed the Cardinal? Tell me! You look terrible!'

'Are you ready for this, Athos?' said d'Artagnan, falling on to a chair. 'Milady's shoulder is branded!'

Athos put his hands over his face. 'Oh no! Surely she isn't . . .'

'Are you sure that your friend's wife – your wife – is dead? Milady's about twenty-eight, blonde with blue eyes.'

'It's her, I think! I must see her, d'Artagnan!'

'Don't go near her, Athos! You nearly killed her once, and she'll want to take her revenge. I'm afraid that I've made a terrible enemy in that woman – an enemy for us both!'

'You're right,' said Athos. 'We must both be very careful for the next two days. After that we'll be with the army, fighting the English. And then it won't matter if it's Milady or the English army who kills us!'

When d'Artagnan went back to his room, Planchet gave him a short letter from the Cardinal.

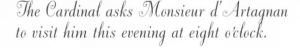

*The Cardinal asks Monsieur d'Artagnan to visit him this evening at eight o'clock.*

'Hmm,' said d'Artagnan. 'What's the Cardinal's plan? Perhaps he'll put me in prison! But I will go to see him. I can always take my friends with me.'

That evening Athos, Porthos and Aramis waited outside the Cardinal's palace, while d'Artagnan went in for his meeting. The great man was alone in his office when d'Artagnan walked in.

'Ah, d'Artagnan. I've heard a lot about you. You had some special business in England a few weeks ago, I understand?'

'You know about that, sir?' asked d'Artagnan.

'My **spies** are everywhere. I haven't **punished** you yet . . .'

'That's very good of you, sir.'

'. . . because I can see that you're brave and **intelligent**. And I have a job for you, d'Artagnan. Would you like to be a captain in my army?'

'Sir, that's very kind of you, but . . .'

'Well, man, come on, come on! Give me your answer!'

'. . . I'm going to become a King's musketeer, sir.'

'There's no difference between my soldiers and the King's,' replied the Cardinal coldly. 'But I see that you want to stay with your friends. Soon the war between France and England will begin, and many soldiers will die. If you are still alive after the fighting, I'll ask you about this again. Goodbye, young man.'

When d'Artagnan told his friends about this conversation, they all agreed he was right to say no to the Cardinal. But d'Artagnan knew that the Cardinal was **warning** him to be careful.

The King's musketeers spent the next month fighting the English, who were in the French town of La Rochelle. D'Artagnan was fighting with his friends, and several times he had a lucky escape from death. He knew that his attackers weren't English soldiers, but Milady's men. Every night, before he went to sleep, he tried to think of a way of finding Constance and punishing Milady at the same time.

**spy** a person who tries to learn secret things

**punish** to hurt someone because they have done something wrong

**intelligent** quick-thinking

**warn** to tell someone about danger or about a bad thing that may happen

One evening Athos, Porthos, and Aramis were on **guard duty** outside the town. They saw a carriage drive up to an **inn**. A lady got out and went into the inn. Soon afterwards a gentleman arrived, got off his horse, and went in. Lights went on in the lady's room.

'That man looked like the Cardinal!' said Aramis.

'And that woman looked like . . . Milady!' said Athos. 'Let's go nearer and listen to what they're saying.'

Luckily the window was open, and the three musketeers could hear every word of the conversation.

'This is very important, Milady,' said the Cardinal. 'You must go at once to England, to see Buckingham. Tell him that if the English go on attacking France, I'll tell the world about him and the Queen.'

'But what if he doesn't listen, and goes on attacking us?'

'An intelligent woman like you can find a way of stopping him.'

'Ah, I understand. Well, sir, a man for a man, a life for a life, help me to kill my enemy and I'll help you to kill yours!'

'Who is your enemy, Milady?'

**guard duty**
watching out for the enemy

**inn** an old name for a hotel where you can eat, drink, or stay

28

'That evil little d'Artagnan! He must die!'

'Do what you like with him. I'll give you a letter to say that you're free to punish him in any way.'

The Cardinal gave Milady a piece of paper and left the room. The musketeers hid behind a wall and watched him ride away.

'Follow him and see where he's going,' Athos told Aramis and Porthos. 'I'll stay here for a while.' The two friends rode off after the Cardinal, and Athos went into the inn. He walked at once into the lady's room without knocking.

'Who are you? What do you want?' cried Milady, afraid.

'Yes, it's her,' Athos said to himself. He took off his hat and walked up to her. 'Do you know who I am?' he asked.

Milady went deathly white. 'Yes – yes, I do!' she cried.

He put his gun to her head. 'Evil one! I know that you're the Cardinal's spy, and I know what you're planning! But d'Artagnan's my friend! If you hurt him, I'll kill you! Give me the Cardinal's letter!'

With a shaking hand she gave it to him, and he left the room.

*The musketeers could hear every word.*

## READING CHECK

**1 Correct the mistakes in these sentences.**

              *Athos*

**a** D'Artagnan tells ~~Porthos~~ about Milady's shoulder.

**b** The King sends a letter asking d'Artagnan to visit him at eight o'clock.

**c** The Cardinal asks de Tréville to be a captain in his army.

**d** The musketeers and d'Artagnan go to fight the Germans in La Rochelle.

**e** Milady's men attack Athos several times.

**f** The Cardinal asks the Queen to speak to Buckingham.

**g** The Cardinal gives Milady a letter saying that she can punish Buckingham in any way.

**h** The musketeers listen to the Cardinal talking to Athos.

**i** Aramis takes the Cardinal's letter from Milady.

**2 Who says this? Who do they say it to? Choose from the names below.**

**a** ☐ 3 'I've heard a lot about you.'

**b** ☐ 'I'm going to become one of the King's musketeers.'

**c** ☐ 'Milady's shoulder is branded.'

**d** ☐ 'Who are you? What do you want?'

**e** ☐ 'Evil one!'

**f** ☐ 'Help me to kill my enemy and I'll help you to kill yours.'

**1** D'Artagnan to the Cardinal

**2** Milady to Athos

**3** the Cardinal to d'Artagnan

**4** Milady to the Cardinal

**5** D'Artagnan to Athos

**6** Athos to Milady

## WORD WORK

**Use the words in the hat to complete the sentences.**

**a** Milady and the Cardinal meet in an
*inn*.................

**b** Milady is the Cardinal's ........................

**c** The Cardinal is an evil but
........................ man.

**d** He decides not to ........................
d'Artagnan for working for the Queen.

**e** The Cardinal ........................ d'Artagnan
not to work against him any more.

**f** The three musketeers are on ............
............ in La Rochelle when Milady arrives.

*spy*
*punish*
*warns guard duty*
*intelligent*
*inn*

## GUESS WHAT

**What happens in the next chapter? Tick the best answers.**

**a** Why are the three musketeers worried?

**1** ☐ Because the Queen is ill.

**2** ☐ Because Milady wants to kill
d'Artagnan.

**3** ☐ Because the English are going to
attack La Rochelle.

**b** What do the musketeers do while the
English are getting ready to attack?

**1** ☐ They eat and drink.

**2** ☐ They run away.

**3** ☐ They get ready to fight.

**c** What happens to the Cardinal's letter?

**1** ☐ The musketeers burn it.

**2** ☐ The musketeers lose it.

**3** ☐ The musketeers decide to put it
in a safe place.

**d** What do the musketeers do?

**1** ☐ They write to the Queen
and to Lord de Winter.

**2** ☐ They write to the King
and the Cardinal.

**3** ☐ They kill Milady.

**e** What happens to d'Artagnan?

**1** ☐ He goes to prison.

**2** ☐ He dies.

**3** ☐ De Tréville wants him to
be a musketeer.

# Chapter 6 *A picnic in the castle*

*W*hen d'Artagnan met the three musketeers the next morning, he saw that they were all looking worried. 'What's happened?' he asked.

'We'll tell you later,' said Athos. 'But first we need to find a safe place where we can talk. There are too many of the Cardinal's spies round here. Where can we go? I know! Let's have a **picnic** in the **castle** of La Rochelle! Our men drove the English away from it yesterday, so it'll be quiet now.'

'But the English will want to attack it again!' said Porthos.

'Well, if they do, then we can fight them,' replied Athos.

'And it is true that nobody will listen to us there,' said Aramis.

***

So a few minutes later the four friends left the French **camp** and crossed a field, where dead bodies lay from the fighting of the day before. Then they climbed a hill to the castle. Behind them came Planchet, carrying a large, heavy **basket** of bread, meat, fruit, and some bottles of good **wine**.

'Here we are!' said Athos, when they arrived at the top of the castle. 'Up here we can easily see if someone's planning to attack us. Is breakfast ready, Planchet? I'm as hungry as a horse!'

They sat on the ground and started eating.

'Tell me your news, Athos!' said d'Artagnan. 'I must know what you've been doing!'

'It's important,' replied Athos. 'We saw Milady outside La Rochelle last night.'

D'Artagnan dropped his glass of wine. 'You saw Milady!'

'Who is Milady?' asked Porthos.

**picnic** a meal that people eat outside in the country, often sitting on the ground

**castle** a large old building with strong, high walls

**camp** a place where soldiers stay in tents for a short time

**basket** a box for carrying food

**wine** a red or white alcoholic drink made from grapes

# DOMINOES

## Audio Download

### Level Two

# The Three Musketeers

## To download the audio for this title

1 Go to www.oup.com/elt/download
2 Use this code and your email address

Your download code

ISBN 978-0-19-465275-9

OXFORD
UNIVERSITY PRESS

'She's an evil woman who wants to take her revenge on d'Artagnan. Last night she asked the Cardinal to help her to kill him.'

'What?' cried d'Artagnan. 'Then there's no hope for me. My enemies are too powerful! I must get ready to die!'

'Forget about that for the moment,' said Aramis. 'Look down there! The English are going to attack the castle!'

'Well, I'm going to finish this wine and chicken first,' said Athos. He finished eating and drinking, then put down his empty glass, and took up his gun. 'Now, musketeers, let's show them!'

**Bang**! Bang! Two of the English soldiers fell. Bang! Bang! Two more lay dead, and soon the rest were running away very fast.

'More wine please, Planchet,' said Athos, sitting down again. 'Now where were we? Ah yes. The Cardinal is sending

*'I'm going to finish this wine and chicken first.'*

**bang** the noise a gun makes

33

Milady to England, to talk to, and possibly to murder, the Duke of Buckingham.'

'Murder him?' said d'Artagnan, horrified. 'But what can we do to stop her?'

'Well, to start with, I've taken the Cardinal's letter away from her. Here it is.' Athos put it on the ground in front of them. They all looked at it.

> *Nobody can punish the person who carries this letter for what they have done.*
>
> *Richelieu*
> *3 December 1627*

'The owner of this letter is free to do anything! She can kill anyone she wants to,' said Aramis.

'Yes, so we must put this letter in a very safe place,' said Athos.

Just then Planchet called out, 'The enemy is attacking again!' Twenty English soldiers were running across the field towards the hill.

'Guns at the ready!' said Athos. 'Now!' Bang! Four soldiers dropped to the ground, and a few minutes later – bang! – three more fell. But the rest were now climbing up the hill towards the castle.

'Over here, all of you!' cried Athos, running to one of the castle walls. The wall was very old, and some of the stones were missing.

'Stand by this wall, and when I say "Push," push as hard as you can! You too, Planchet!' The five men pushed against the heavy wall, and it fell with a great crash on to the heads of the enemy. There were terrible cries, and then all was quiet.

Athos put an arm round d'Artagnan, who was looking

*The five men pushed against the heavy wall.*

down sadly at the dead men. 'It's war, you know, my friend,' he said. 'Perhaps it'll be us tomorrow! Now, gentlemen, we need to think of a plan.'

'Yes,' said Porthos. 'I'd like to kill Milady. We won't be safe while she's alive. She doesn't know me, so I can easily get near her.'

'Kill a woman!' cried Aramis. 'I don't like that. No, I have a much better plan. We must tell the Queen that Buckingham's life is in danger.'

'How will that help the rest of us?' asked Porthos.

'I know!' said Athos. 'Milady has an English brother-in-law, Lord de Winter. We can warn him that she's planning to kill Buckingham. Then he can watch her carefully, or even lock her up.'

'Wonderful!' cried d'Artagnan. 'Let's write two letters, then. One to the Queen, and one to Lord de Winter. Who'll write them?'

'Aramis is a good letter writer. He writes a lot of love letters,' said Porthos, smiling.

'I don't!' said Aramis. 'But I can write a good letter, it's true.'

An hour later, the two letters were ready. When Aramis read them aloud to the others, Athos said, 'Aramis, you're the king of letter-writers!'

'I'll send the Queen's letter to one of my friends,' said Aramis, 'who can give it to the Queen.'

'A lady friend, perhaps?' smiled d'Artagnan. 'And Planchet can take Lord de Winter's letter to England for us.'

༄❀༉

When the friends arrived back at the French camp, they found that Monsieur de Tréville was waiting for them.

'Everybody's talking about your brave fighting at the castle!' he said. 'D'Artagnan, I'd like you to become one of the King's musketeers at once!'

D'Artagnan and his three friends were **delighted**.

༄❀༉

While they were listening to this news, Milady was sailing to England. Unluckily for her, a storm **damaged** the ship that she was in. So her journey took her much longer than usual, and she arrived there on the same day that Planchet left England to go back to France. Lord de Winter had already read the letter from the musketeers.

So when Milady reached England, Lord de Winter's men were waiting for her. They took her to his castle, where they locked her in a room with a strong wooden door. She was now a prisoner.

*'I can write a good letter, it's true.'*

## READING CHECK

**Match the sentences with the people.**

**1** The Cardinal

**3** Lord de Winter

**4** The Queen

**a** Planchet carries food and wine for ..b..

**b** ...... and ...... push the castle wall onto the English.

**c** Athos tells the others about Milady's meeting with ......

**d** Athos tells the others that Milady is going to meet and perhaps kill ......

**e** Athos takes out ......'s letter for the others to read.

**f** Aramis writes two letters. One to ...... and one to ......

**g** ...... takes Lord de Winter's letter to England.

**h** ...... puts Milady in prison.

**2** Planchet

**5** Buckingham

**6** The musketeers

## WORD WORK

**Find words in the road to complete the sentences.**

**a** There is a <u>castle</u> on the hill in La Rochelle.

**b** The musketeers decide to have a _ _ _ _ _ _ there.

**c** Planchet carries the _ _ _ _ _ _ with all the food and drink in it.

**d** They take some bottles of good _ _ _ _ with them.

**e** There are a lot of the Cardinal's spies in the French _ _ _ _ so they don't want to talk there.

**f** The musketeers are _ _ _ _ _ _ _ _ _ _ when they hear that d'Artagnan is going to be a musketeer.

**g** A storm _ _ _ _ _ _ _ _ the ship that Milady is travelling on.

**h** '_ _ _ _' is the sound that a gun makes when you shoot it.

## GUESS WHAT

**What happens in the next chapter? Tick the boxes.**

**a** Milady leaves prison because she ☐ talks to Lord de Winter.
☐ escapes.

**b** Milady ☐ kills
☐ asks someone to kill Buckingham.

**c** ☐ The Queen
☐ The Cardinal sends a letter to Buckingham asking him to stop the war between England and France.

**d** Milady goes back to France and meets ☐ Constance Bonacieux.
☐ the Queen.

**e** Milady becomes Constance's ☐ friend.
☐ enemy.

# Chapter 7  Milady at work

M ilady looked round her room, horrified. 'Why has de Winter brought me here? Someone has told him of my plans! I must get out of here!' Just then the door opened, and a young army captain came in. Suddenly Milady was no longer afraid. 'Ah!' she thought, smiling to herself. 'Perhaps I can **persuade** him to help me escape!'

'Good morning, Milady,' said the young captain. 'I'm John Felton. Lord de Winter has sent me to **guard** you, day and night.'

'I understand, sir,' said Milady. 'I hope that I won't be any trouble to you. I've done nothing wrong, so I have nothing to fear from **God** or Lord de Winter. Leave me now. It's time for me to **pray**.' She closed her eyes, put her hands together, and **pretended** to pray.

John Felton left the room, looking surprised. 'Lord de Winter told me that she was evil!' he thought. 'Perhaps he's wrong!'

Every day for the next week, Felton visited Milady. Each time she pretended that she was praying, and did not look at him. In the end she looked up when he came in. He saw her beautiful face, and felt very sorry for her.

'Go on praying,' he said. 'God will look kindly on your crimes.'

'My crimes? Sir, you don't understand! It's other people who need God's help, not me! I am praying for them!'

'What do you mean, Lady de Winter?'

'I'll tell you everything, sir. This is what happened to me. When I was young and, unluckily, beautiful, a man fell in love with me. He kidnapped me and hoped to persuade me

**persuade** to make somebody change their way of thinking

**guard** to watch a prisoner and to stop him or her from running away

**God** an important person who never dies and who decides what happens in the world

**pray** to speak privately to God

**pretend** to try to make somebody believe something

to marry him. He found that he couldn't persuade me, so he began to **seduce** me, but I fought against him. "All right, I'll let you go!" he said angrily in the end. "You'll never love me, I can see that!"

"I'll tell the world that you kidnapped me!" I told him.

"But nobody will listen to you if they think that you're a criminal!" he replied. And with a hot **iron** he branded my shoulder!'

'Who was this evil man?' asked Felton, horrified.

'The – the Duke of Buckingham!' said Milady softly.

*He saw her beautiful face, and felt very sorry for her.*

**seduce** to persuade or to force someone to have sex with you

**iron** a metal stick which is used to burn someone

41

'And why is Lord de Winter keeping you a prisoner?'

'His brother fell in love with me and I told him my terrible secret. But he died soon after we married, so he didn't have time to tell Lord de Winter. I think that Buckingham has told de Winter to keep me here for a while, and then kill me or send me to Carolina for life!'

Felton kissed Milady's hand. 'You are an **angel**! Here's one man who will fight for you! I'll help you to escape! And, with God's help, I'll take revenge on Buckingham for you, too!'

Milady was delighted that her plan was working. That night Felton came quietly to her room and helped her to get out of the window. He climbed down to the ground, carrying her on his back. From there they ran across a field to the sea, where a ship was waiting for them.

Felton spoke to the ship's captain. 'Sail to Portsmouth,' he said. 'I have business there, so you must wait for me. Then when I'm back on the ship again, we can sail to France!'

At Portsmouth, a large town by the sea in the south of England, the English army was getting ready to attack France. There were hundreds of ships, full of soldiers, waiting for the Duke of Buckingham to tell them to sail. Buckingham himself was there, staying at one of the inns. Felton went to this inn. He asked to see the Duke at once, and the servant showed him into the Duke's room.

'Sir, I've come about Lady de Winter,' he told the Duke.

'That evil woman!' said Buckingham, angrily. 'But what are you—'

'Not evil, sir! She's an angel! You're the evil one! God will punish you because you kidnapped her! You seduced her! You branded her! And now you'll die for your crimes!' And Felton took out a knife and pushed it deep into Buckingham's **chest**.

**angel** a very good and beautiful person; in pictures they usually have wings

**chest** the top half of the front part of the body

'Patrick, help me, I'm dying!' the Duke called to his servant. At that moment Patrick ran into the room, saying, 'Sir, a letter from France!'

'Is it from the Queen?' asked Buckingham. 'Tell me what she says!'

'Sir, you're hurt! Let me call a doctor!' said the servant.

'No, it's too late. Tell me, Patrick! There isn't much time!'

'Sir, she says, "Please stop this war and **save** the lives of hundreds of English and French people. Be careful. Your life is in danger. Stay alive for the day when you are no longer my enemy."'

The Duke was losing blood fast. 'Is that all, is that all?' he asked with difficulty. 'Is there nothing more?'

'Sir, she says that she still loves you.'

'Thank God,' said Buckingham. 'Then my death will really mean something to her.' And smiling a last smile, he died.

⁂

When Lord de Winter arrived at his castle, he found out about Milady's escape. He rode as fast as he could to Portsmouth, but arrived just too late to stop Felton and save the Duke's life.

While Buckingham lay dying, Milady's ship was on its way to France. 'The English will catch Felton and hang him for murder, but he's done good work for me and the Cardinal,' Milady thought. 'When we arrive in France, I must go to **Béthune**. I hear that the Queen has moved that stupid little Bonacieux woman to the **convent** there.'

When Milady arrived at the convent, she asked to meet Madame Bonacieux, and was very kind to the lonely young woman. Soon the two women were spending most of their time together, and Milady pretended to be Constance's dearest friend. They talked about everything, and Constance told Milady how much she loved a young man called d'Artagnan, one of the King's musketeers.

**save** to take someone out of danger

**Béthune** /be'tʃuːn/

**convent** a church building where women (called nuns) live, work and pray; in the past, a convent was a safe place for a woman in danger

*'How happy I am!'*

'He's coming here soon, you know!' she said excitedly.

'What? Here?' cried Milady. 'Impossible! He's at La Rochelle!'

'So you know him as well, Milady! Is he – was he – in love with you too? Tell me! I must know!'

'Oh no, I just know him as a friend.' Milady had to think quickly. 'He told me all about you, the love of his life! So now at last I've met you, dear Constance! How happy I am!' And she held the young woman in her arms, smiling lovingly at her.

One day a gentleman arrived at the convent and asked to see Milady. He was Rochefort, one of the Cardinal's men, and he came to give Milady a letter from the Cardinal. She asked him to send a carriage for her an hour later. When he left, he passed four men riding fast towards the convent. They were d'Artagnan and his friends.

'Look!' cried d'Artagnan. 'It's the man from Meung again!'

'He's dropped a piece of paper,' said Porthos. 'It says **Armentières**. That's a village near here, I think.'

'No time to follow him, gentlemen!' said Athos. 'Let's find Madame Bonacieux first!'

⚜

At the convent Milady was talking to Constance. 'Listen to me, my dear. We're both in great danger!'

'Oh dear! How do you know?' Constance looked afraid.

'The man who visited me just now was my brother. He told me that the Cardinal's men are coming to take us both away!'

'But d'Artagnan is coming to save me! He'll be here soon!'

'No, my dear, he isn't coming. The Cardinal's men will arrive dressed as musketeers and take us to prison, if we don't get away!'

'How terrible! Dear Lady de Winter, don't you have a plan?'

'I have, my dear. My brother's sending his carriage in half an hour, and I'm going off in it to hide somewhere a few miles from here. Why don't you come with me?'

'Very well. How good you are, Milady! Thank you!'

'Now, go to your room and pack any little things that you want to take with you – d'Artagnan's love-letters, for example.'

Constance hurried to her room, while Milady stood by the window, looking down at the road. 'Will Rochefort's carriage or the musketeers get here first?' she thought. 'Will I be able to stop d'Artagnan saving his Constance? What about my revenge? Let's see what happens!'

**Armentières**
/ɑːmɒnˈtjeə/

## READING CHECK

**Choose the right words to complete the sentences.**

**a** Milady tells John Felton that . . .
kidnapped her when she was younger.

1 ☐ the Cardinal
2 ☑ the Duke of Buckingham
3 ☐ Lord de Winter

**b** Milady gets . . . to help her escape.

1 ☐ John Felton
2 ☐ Lord de Winter
3 ☐ the Cardinal

**c** . . . kills Buckingham.

1 ☐ John Felton
2 ☐ Milady
3 ☐ The Cardinal

**d** The Duke of Buckingham's servant Patrick
brings him a letter from . . .

1 ☐ the King of France.
2 ☐ the Queen of France.
3 ☐ the Cardinal.

**e** Buckingham dies feeling . . .

1 ☐ happy.
2 ☐ sad.
3 ☐ angry.

**f** Milady goes to find . . . in Béthune.

1 ☐ the Queen
2 ☐ Constance Bonacieux
3 ☐ d'Artagnan

**g** Milady tells Constance that d'Artagnan
is her . . .

1 ☐ cousin.
2 ☐ lover.
3 ☐ friend.

**h** Milady tells Constance that . . . are
coming to take her away.

1 ☐ the musketeers
2 ☐ the Cardinal's men
3 ☐ the English

## WORD WORK

**Use the words in the prison wall to complete Milady's diary.**

angel  convent  guarding  iron  persuade  prayed  pretended  save  seduce

It will not be hard to escape from this prison. Today I talked with Felton, the young man who is **(a)** ...guarding. me. Perhaps I can **(b)** ........................ him to help me. I **(c)** ........................ to be a very good woman and I said that I went to church and that I **(d)** ........................ there every day. I also told him 'Buckingham tried to **(e)** ........................ me when I was younger and he branded my shoulder with a hot **(f)** ........................ .' After I finished my story Felton looked at me and called me 'an **(g)** ........................'. When I escape from here, Buckingham will die. Then I will find Constance. I think she is living in a **(h)** ........................ in France now. I will use her to get d'Artagnan to come to me. Nothing and nobody will **(i)** ........................ d'Artagnan then. He will die in my arms!

## GUESS WHAT

**What happens in the next chapter? Tick the boxes.**

**a** Milady kills ☐ Constance. ☐ d'Artagnan.

**b** ☐ Constance ☐ Milady runs away before the ☐ musketeers ☐ Cardinal's men arrive.

**c** ☐ Milady ☐ Constance dies in ☐ d'Artagnan's ☐ Athos's arms.

**d** The musketeers, d'Artagnan and de Winter go to find ☐ Milady. ☐ the Cardinal.

**e** In the end ☐ Milady ☐ The Cardinal must die.

# Chapter 8 Revenge

When Constance came back into the room, Milady persuaded her to eat some chicken and drink a glass of wine. Suddenly they heard the sound of horses on the road. Milady ran to the window. She could see that the riders were the four musketeers. 'It's the Cardinal's men!' she said. 'Quick! We must escape through the garden! Follow me!'

But poor Constance could not move. 'Go without me, Milady!' she cried. 'Save yourself! I'm so afraid! I can't stand up!'

'Leave you here? Never!' replied Milady bravely. She opened the stone on her ring, and secretly put some **poison** from it into Constance's unfinished wine. Then she held the glass to the young woman's mouth, and with a smile, helped Constance to drink it. 'Revenge is sweet,' Milady thought, and she ran out of the room.

A few minutes later, d'Artagnan ran into the room. 'Constance, I've found you at last!' he cried, taking the young woman in his arms.

'D'Artagnan, is it really you? I can't see you very well! I'm ill!'

D'Artagnan turned to his friends. 'What can I do? Her hands are cold. She's **fainting**! Help me, all of you!'

Athos was looking horrified at the nearly empty wine glass on the table. 'I think there's poison in this glass! Poor woman, poor woman!' he said.

'She's opening her eyes again!' said d'Artagnan.

'Madame, who put the wine in this glass?' asked Athos.

'My dear friend, who's been here with me. Lady de Winter.'

'No!' the musketeers cried out together. At that moment

**poison** something that kills people when they eat or drink it

**faint** to fall down suddenly because you are weak, ill, afraid or horrified

Constance's face went grey and she fell from her chair to the ground.

'Where are you, d'Artagnan? Hold me! I'm dying!' she cried.

D'Artagnan held her in his arms. 'I'm here, Constance! I'll never leave you! Porthos, Aramis, Athos, get a doctor at once!'

'I'm sorry, d'Artagnan,' said Athos. 'We can't do anything for her now.'

Constance took d'Artagnan's head in her hands and kissed him once, lovingly. Then, with a last **sigh**, she died. D'Artagnan closed his eyes and lay down on the floor next to her.

Suddenly a man hurried into the room. 'Gentlemen,' he said, 'I'm Lord de Winter, and, like you, I'm looking for Milady.' He saw the two bodies on the ground. 'Are they both dead?' he asked.

'No,' said Athos. 'D'Artagnan's only fainted.'

Just then d'Artagnan's eyes opened. He took Constance in his arms again, and started crying over her body.

'D'Artagnan, be a man,' said Athos softly. 'Only women cry for the dead. Men take their revenge.'

**sigh** to breathe once, very deeply

*With a last sigh, she died.*

49

'I'm with you, if you're planning revenge,' said d'Artagnan.

Athos asked the head of the convent to **arrange** a **funeral** for Madame Bonacieux. Then the five men left the convent, talking about what to do next. Porthos, Aramis, and de Winter wanted to follow Milady at once, to catch her and to punish her. But Athos didn't agree.

'Leave it to me,' he said. 'I'll arrange everything.'

'But I must help you,' said de Winter. 'After all, she is my sister-in-law.'

'And she is my wife,' said Athos, and he quickly told his story. Porthos and Aramis were horrified to hear it. 'There's an inn in this village, so we can stay here tonight,' Athos went on. 'You can safely leave me – Milady's husband – to find her. Oh, d'Artagnan, do you have that piece of paper? You remember, the man from Meung dropped it.'

'Of course!' said d'Artagnan excitedly. 'It has the name of a village on it, in Milady's writing. Here it is.'

The five men went to their bedrooms at the inn, but Athos couldn't sleep. He was planning his attack on Milady. First he called the musketeers' servants to his room, and told them to go to the village of Armentières. Their job was to find out where Milady was staying, and to guard her. Then he put on his sword and **cloak**, and left the inn.

He took the road out of the village into the country. Sometimes he had to ask the way. But at last he arrived at a dark, silent house, and knocked on the door. A tall man with black hair let him in. He lived here alone, with no family or servants, a long way from any other people. Athos sat down and explained what he wanted the man to do. At first the man shook his head. But when Athos showed him the Cardinal's letter, the man thought for a moment, and then agreed. Athos thanked him, and walked back to the inn.

**arrange** to make a plan for something to happen

**funeral** the time when a dead person is put under the ground

**cloak** a coat with no arms

The next day the four friends and de Winter went to Constance's funeral at the convent. Athos told them to be ready to leave that evening. So, at eight o'clock, d'Artagnan, Aramis, Porthos and de Winter were waiting for Athos outside the inn. They were surprised to see Athos ride towards them with another man. He was tall, with a **mask** over his face and wearing a long blue cloak. Nobody asked Athos any questions, and all six of them rode to Armentières.

When they arrived at the village, Planchet took them to a small house near the river. Milady was staying there, and the other servants were on guard duty, in the fields around the house.

With a great shout, Athos broke one of the windows, and jumped through. At the same time d'Artagnan broke down the door, and the others followed him. When she saw them all inside the house, Milady gave a cry, and fell down on to a chair. D'Artagnan lifted his gun and held it to her head.

'Don't shoot, d'Artagnan!' cried Athos. 'We're going to **try** this woman, not murder her!'

'Don't shoot, d'Artagnan!'

51

'What do you want, all of you?' cried Milady, afraid.

'We want to try you for your crimes,' said Athos, 'and if we decide you are **guilty**, then we'll punish you. D'Artagnan, I call you to speak first!'

D'Artagnan came forward. 'This woman gave poison to Constance Bonacieux, who died yesterday. She tried to kill me three times at La Rochelle, because she hated me!'

'We agree that d'Artagnan's story is all true,' said Porthos and Aramis.

'Now, Lord de Winter, please say something,' said Athos.

'This woman arranged the murder of the Duke of Buckingham. Some years ago she also killed her husband, my brother, with poison!'

'How evil!' cried Porthos and Aramis.

Athos himself now came forward. 'This woman was my wife, until I found out that she was branded!'

Milady jumped up and cried, 'I'm not a criminal! You'll never find the man who branded me! Show me that man, if you can!'

At this, the man in the blue cloak came forward. 'I'm the man who branded you,' he said, taking off his mask.

Milady looked silently at him for a moment. Then she screamed, 'No, it can't be! It's – it's the **executioner** of Lille!'

He turned to the others and explained. 'Yes, I'm the executioner in the town of Lille. This woman was branded, when she was much younger, for a number of evil crimes.'

Now Athos spoke. 'How shall we punish her?' he asked.

'She must die!' said d'Artagnan, and the others all agreed.

'Milady,' said Athos, 'we have found you guilty of your crimes. Get ready to die. If you know how to pray, do it now.'

Milady knew that there was no more hope. The executioner's strong hand fell on her shoulder. Quietly all of them walked out of the little house, and down to the

**guilty** who has done something wrong

**executioner** a person whose job is to kill criminals

river. They watched the executioner lift his heavy sword high in the air, and bring it down once on Milady's proud neck. Carefully he put his blue cloak round the dead body, and carried it into the deep water in the middle of the river. The body went down like a stone.

Now that Buckingham was dead, and the war with England was over, the musketeers went back to Paris, where life went on as usual. Sometimes d'Artagnan sighed unhappily over his lost love, but his friends always helped him to feel better.

'There are other pretty women, you know,' smiled Aramis.

'And more adventures for brave musketeers like us!' said Porthos.

'We'll fight for France, and for our King and Queen!' said Athos.

'One for all, and all for one!' they all shouted together.

*'One for all, and all for one!'*

## READING CHECK

**What do they say?**

① I'm not a criminal!

② Milady is my wife.

③ She killed my brother with poison.

④ Hold me! I'm dying!

⑤ She tried to kill me three times at La Rochelle.

⑥ This woman was branded for a number of evil crimes.

⑦ We agree that d'Artagnan's story is all true!

a ...'Hold me! I'm dying!'... says Constance to d'Artagnan.

b .................................................... says Athos to the others.

c .................................................... says Milady.

d .................................................... says Lord de Winter.

e .................................................... says d'Artagnan.

f .................................................... say Porthos and Aramis.

g .................................................... the executioner of Lille tells everyone.

## WORD WORK

**Complete the sentences with the pairs of words.**

tried  poisoning   ~~fainted  sigh~~   arranged  funeral   cloak  mask   guilty  executioner

a  With a deep ..sigh.... Constance died and d'Artagnan .fainted.. at once.

b  The head of the convent ................ Constance's ................ .

**c** The man from Lille had a ...............
over his head and he wore a long blue
.................

**d** The musketeers ............... Milady
for ............... her husband and
Constance, and for other terrible
crimes.

**e** They decided Milady was ............... and the ................... of Lille cut off her head.

# Project A · *A Diary Page*

**1 Read Planchet's diary. Which page of the story does it come from?**

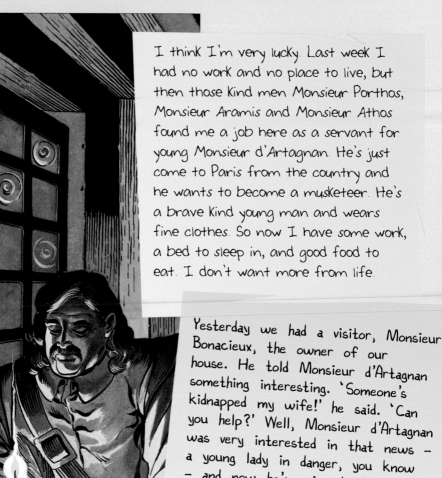

I think I'm very lucky. Last week I had no work and no place to live, but then those kind men Monsieur Porthos, Monsieur Aramis and Monsieur Athos found me a job here as a servant for young Monsieur d'Artagnan. He's just come to Paris from the country and he wants to become a musketeer. He's a brave kind young man and wears fine clothes. So now I have some work, a bed to sleep in, and good food to eat. I don't want more from life.

Yesterday we had a visitor, Monsieur Bonacieux, the owner of our house. He told Monsieur d'Artagnan something interesting. 'Someone's kidnapped my wife!' he said. 'Can you help?' Well, Monsieur d'Artagnan was very interested in that news – a young lady in danger, you know – and now he's going to look for Madame Bonacieux. We had chicken for supper.

**2  Put these adjectives into the correct column. Use a dictionary to help you.**

| PLANCHET | | D'ARTAGNAN |
|---|---|---|
| ..................... | brave | ..................... |
| ..................... | practical | ..................... |
| ..................... | idealistic | ..................... |
| ..................... | kind | ..................... |
| ..................... | romantic | ..................... |
| ..................... | down-to-earth | ..................... |
| ..................... | proud | ..................... |
| ..................... | humble | ..................... |

**3  Complete this page from Planchet's diary.**

This morning Monsieur d'Artagnan and his friends decided
they wanted to have a picnic **(a)** .....................
I had to carry a basket of **(b)** .....................
We walked across **(c)** .....................
and then we walked up **(d)**.....................
I was very tired when we got there.
During the picnic the English **(e)** .....................
The musketeers **(f)**.....................
Then the English attacked again, and we pushed
**(g)**.....................
The musketeers weren't afraid, but I **(h)**.....................
After the picnic we **(i)**.....................

**4  Now write another page from Planchet's diary from a different part of the story.**

## Project B    *Past Times*

**1   Look at this project on life in England in the 1600s and complete the sentences.**

# England in the 1600s

**Oliver Cromwell** ruled England from 1653. People asked him to become king but he said 'no'. In 1658 he ................

**Charles I** was king of ................ and Scotland from 1625. He thought that kings could do what they wanted without asking parliament.

In 1660 England brought back **King Charles II** (Charles I's son) who was living in Holland. He was a king who loved pleasure.

**Nell Gwynn** was a ................ actress and friend of Charles II.

**Cavaliers** and **Roundheads**
From 1642-1649 there was a
Civil War in England between
the long-haired 'cavaliers'
(fighting for the king) and the
short-haired 'roundheads'
(fighting for parliament).
Soldiers fought with ................
and muskets. They rode horses.

**John Milton**
was a famous poet at this time.
He ................. 'Paradise Lost'.

The famous Dutch painter
**Van Dyck** lived and
........................ pictures in
England at this time.

**The roundheads** won the war and in 1649 the
executioner cut off King Charles I's ................. .

**2  Choose a time in the history of your country and make notes.**

Your country: _____

Time in history: _____

Rulers _____     Politics _____
_____     _____
_____     _____
_____     _____
_____     _____
_____     _____
_____     _____

Wars _____     Transport _____
_____     _____
_____     _____
_____     _____
_____     _____
_____     _____

Artists and Writers _____     Fashion _____
_____     _____
_____     _____
_____     _____
_____     _____
_____     _____
_____     _____

**3  Use your notes to make a project about this time in the history
of your country. Use the project on pages 58–59 to help you.**

## GRAMMAR CHECK

### Past Simple: affirmative

We use the Past Simple to talk about things that happened at a specific time in the past and that are now finished.

*D'Artagnan's son talked to Monsieur de Tréville.*

With regular verbs, we usually add –d/–ed to the infinitive without to.

*A young man called d'Artagnan arrived in Paris. He visited Monsieur de Tréville.*

With regular verbs that end in consonant + –y, we change the y to i and add –ed.

*carry – The musketeers always carried their swords with them.*

Some verbs are irregular. You must learn their past forms.

*steal – Someone stole two of the Queen's diamonds.*

**1  Complete d'Artagnan's diary with the Past Simple form of the verbs in brackets.**

> *What an exciting day! First, I a) .....arrived..... (arrive) in the great city of Paris and b) ............... (go) to see the Captain of the King's musketeers. I c) ............... (tell) him that I wanted to join the musketeers. But suddenly, when I d) ............... (look) out of the window, I e) ............... (see) the man who f) ............... (steal) my father's letter from me at Meung! I g) ............... (run) after him. In my hurry, I h) ............... (bump) into a musketeer on the stairs, then I i) ............... (knock) a second musketeer's hat off by accident and, finally, I j) ............... (make) a third man angry by asking about his lady friend! After all that, I k) ............... (lose) the man from Meung. Luckily, the three musketeers l) ............... (decide) not to fight me, and we m) ............... (be) soon good friends. They n) ............... (show) me round Paris. And they even o) ............... (find) a servant for me! Later, the four of us p) ............... (have) dinner together. We q) ............... (drink) a lot of good wine, and we r) ............... (laugh) at everything that s) ............... (happen) today. I think that I'm going to sleep well tonight!*

## GRAMMAR CHECK

### Present Perfect and Past Simple

We use the Present Perfect to talk about things happening at some time in the past without saying when.

*I've thought of a plan. Athos hasn't forgotten his wife.*

We can also use the Present Perfect to talk about things that began in the past and are continuing now.

*I've loved you for a long time. I've never been so happy.* (= at no time in my life)

We use the Past Simple to talk about things that happened at a specific time in the past and that are now finished.

*One evening last week, the Cardinal met Milady in secret.*

**2 Complete the Queen's letter. Use the Present Perfect or Past Simple form of the verbs in brackets.**

My dear Buckingham,
Do you remember the twelve diamonds that I a) ...gave....
(give) you last week? At the time, I b) ............... (want) you
to have some of my things to keep because I c) ...............
(not want) you to forget me. But now the King d) ...............
(explain) to me that there will be an important dinner
soon. He e) ............... (come) to see me an hour ago and he
f) ............... (ask) me to wear the diamonds at the dinner!
I think that the Cardinal g) ............... (speak) to him
yesterday and h) ............... (tell) him that I have a lover! I
i) ............... (never/be) so worried before. I must ask you to
send back the diamonds.
I know that you and I j) ............... (love) each other for years.
But all that must stop now. Please burn any letters that
I k) ............... (write) to you recently, and also this one. I
hope that reading this letter l) ............... (not make) you too
unhappy. Be very careful. Your life is in danger.


Anne

## GRAMMAR CHECK

**Modal auxiliary verbs: can, can't, must, and mustn't**

We use can + infinitive without *to* to talk about things that we are able to do or that are possible.

*I can take you to the house of my friend Athos.*

We use can't + infinitive without *to* to talk about things that we are not able to do or that are not possible.

*We can't talk for long!*

We use must + infinitive without *to* when we think it is necessary or very important to do something, or when it is an obligation.

*The letter must arrive safely in London.*

We use mustn't + infinitive without *to* to talk about things that we think should not happen.

*Milady mustn't take her revenge on d'Artagnan.*

**3 Choose the correct word to complete each sentence.**

**a** D'Artagnan **can't**/**mustn't** keep away from the beautiful Milady.

**b** Kitty feels that she **must/can** warn d'Artagnan that Milady is evil.

**c** D'Artagnan thinks that he **can/can't** find out more about Milady from Kitty.

**d** While he is hiding, d'Artagnan **must/can** hear Milady talking to Kitty.

**e** When d'Artagnan visits Milady as the Count, she **must/mustn't** know who he really is.

**f** Athos tells d'Artagnan that the young man **can't/must** forget Milady.

**g** But d'Artagnan still **mustn't/can't** stop visiting Milady.

**h** Milady tells d'Artagnan that they **must/can** be happy together.

**i** Suddenly she attacks him, but she **can't/mustn't** hurt him.

**j** 'You **must/can** die!' she screams wildly at him.

## GRAMMAR CHECK

**Negative questions**

There are two types of negative question. In the first type, we use can't, won't, don't, or haven't at the beginning of the sentence. Notice the word order for the rest of the question (subject + main verb).

*Can't you tell us why, d'Artagnan?*        *Won't Lord de Winter arrive in time?*

*Don't you love him, Milady?*        *Haven't the musketeers won the fight?*

With the verb be, we use isn't, aren't, wasn't, or weren't.

*Isn't the servant girl pretty?*        *Aren't I brave?*

In the second type of negative question, we start with a question word – usually why – followed by a negative verb.

*Why didn't the King notice?*        *Why isn't d'Artagnan safe from Milady?*

**4** **Write the words in the correct order to make questions.**

**a** push / the / can't / enemy / this / on / we / wall / ?

　　*Can't we push this wall on the enemy?*

**b** they / answer / give / us / can't / the / ?

　　.................................................................................

**c** plan / me / your / you / won't / tell / ?

　　.................................................................................

**d** for / anyone / me / isn't / waiting / ?

　　.................................................................................

**e** aren't / why / married / I / Buckingham / to / ?

　　.................................................................................

**f** Constance / doesn't / and / some / poison / drink / die / ?

　　.................................................................................

**g** had / you / special / England / in / haven't / some / business / ?

　　.................................................................................

## GRAMMAR CHECK

### Question tags

We can use question tags to check information, or to ask someone to agree with us.

*The Queen was at the dinner, wasn't she?*

*This ring's beautiful, isn't it?*

The tag contains subject + main verb, or auxiliary verb, to match the sentence.

*You were in England then, weren't you?*

*Constance hasn't been kidnapped, has she?*

When the sentence is affirmative, the tag is negative.

*Milady is evil, isn't she?*

When the sentence is negative, the tag is affirmative.

*You won't tell anyone my secret, will you?*

**5 Complete the sentences with the question tags from the box.**

| doesn't she | did he | did I | will he | ~~aren't I~~ | isn't he |
|---|---|---|---|---|---|
| won't we | isn't she | wasn't he | haven't they | wasn't I |

**a** I'm going to become a King's musketeer, .....*aren't I*...?

**b** I didn't catch the man from Meung, ............... ?

**c** Buckingham is in love with the Queen, ............... ?

**d** Somebody has stolen the diamonds, ............... ?

**e** The King was angry with the Cardinal, ............... ?

**f** Athos won't fall in love again, ............... ?

**g** Milady's a very beautiful woman, ............... ?

**h** Milady wants to kill me, ............... ?

**i** I was right to say 'no' to the Cardinal, ............... ?

**j** We'll fight the enemy if they attack us, ............... ?

**k** Buckingham didn't seduce Milady, ............... ?

## GRAMMAR CHECK

### Past Continuous and Past Simple with when and while

We use the Past Continuous to talk about longer actions in the past, and the Past Simple to talk about shorter actions in the past.

*Athos was running to one of the castle walls.*

*The five men pushed against the heavy wall.*

We use time expressions to show the relationship between two actions in the past. We use while in front of the Past Continuous verb and when in front of the Past Simple verb.

*Planchet was resting after the fight when he fell asleep.*

*While the three friends were talking, Aramis wrote two letters.*

**6 Complete the sentences. Use the Past Continuous or Past Simple form of the verbs in brackets.**

**a** When d'Artagnan …*ran*… (run) into the room, Constance *was feeling* (feel) ill.

**b** She …………… (faint) when d'Artagnan …………… (ask) his friends for help.

**c** She …………… (find) it very difficult to speak when she …………… (say) the name of Lady de Winter.

**d** While she …………… (die), she …………… (call) for d'Artagnan.

**e** She …………… (give) him a loving kiss while she …………… (lie) in his arms.

**f** While this …………… (happen), Lord de Winter …………… (hurry) into the room.

**g** While d'Artagnan …………… (cry) over Constance's dead body, Athos …………… (try) to make him feel better.

**h** When the four friends …………… (leave) the room, they …………… (talk) about what to do next.

**i** While they …………… (make) their plans, Athos …………… (tell) them that Milady was his wife.

## GRAMMAR CHECK

### Reported speech with say and explain

| In direct speech we give the words that people say. | In reported speech, we begin with that, put the verb one step into the past, and change the pronouns and possessive adjectives. |
|---|---|
| *'I love a young man called d'Artagnan,' said Milady.* | *Milady said that she loved a young man called d'Artagnan.* |
| *'D'Artagnan, I can give you a job,' said the Cardinal.* | *The Cardinal explained that he could give d'Artagnan a job.* |

Note that *now* becomes *then* in reported speech.

**7  Write the sentences again. Use reported speech.**

**a** 'I want to kill Milady now!' said d'Artagnan.

D'Artagnan said that he wanted to kill Milady then.

**b** 'We agree with you, Athos,' said Porthos and Aramis.

...............................................................................................

**c** 'Milady never stops trying to kill me!' said d'Artagnan.

...............................................................................................

.......................

**d** 'She's a branded criminal,' Athos explained.

...............................................................................................

.......................

**e** 'I know you, and you're evil,' said the executioner to Milady.

...............................................................................................

**f** 'We find you guilty, Milady,' Athos explained.

...............................................................................................

**g** 'I don't want to die so young!' said Milady.

...............................................................................................

**h** 'You can pray, if you like,' Athos said to Milady.

...............................................................................................

# DOMINOES Your Choice

Read *Dominoes* for pleasure, or to develop language skills. It's your choice.

Each *Domino* reader includes:
- a good story to enjoy
- integrated activities to develop reading skills and increase vocabulary
- task-based projects – perfect for CEFR portfolios
- contextualized grammar activities

Each *Domino* pack contains a reader, and an excitingly dramatized audio recording of the story

If you liked this *Domino*, read these:

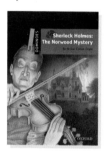

### Sherlock Holmes: The Norwood Mystery
*Sir Arthur Conan Doyle*

'For me, Watson, life is not so interesting,' says Holmes. 'I loved to read the newspaper, hoping to find some news of an interesting crime for me to investigate or a dangerous criminal for me to catch. Where are all those clever criminals these days?'

Then, suddenly, a wild, excited young man runs up the stairs to Holmes' room. He has a story to tell about a strange crime that took place in Norwood. But who is the criminal? And is he dangerous? Life, for Holmes, suddenly starts to get interesting.

### Lord Arthur Savile's Crime and Other Stories
*Oscar Wilde*

The three stories in this book are about ordinary people, people like you and me; but they find themselves in surprising situations. Lord Arthur Savile, a rich man with no enemies, finds out that he must do something terrible before he can marry. Poor young Hughie Erskine gives money to an old beggar – but the beggar is not what he seems. And Lord Murchison falls in love with a mystery woman – but what is the strange secret behind the door in Cumnor Street?

|  | CEFR | Cambridge Exams | IELTS | TOEFL iBT | TOEIC |
|---|---|---|---|---|---|
| Level 3 | B1 | PET | 4.0 | 57-86 | 550 |
| Level 2 | A2–B1 | KET-PET | 3.0-4.0 | – | 390 |
| Level 1 | A1–A2 | YLE Flyers/KET | 3.0 | – | 225 |
| Starter & Quick Starter | A1 | YLE Movers | 1.0–2.0 | – | – |

You can find details and a full list of books and teachers' resources on our website:
www.oup.com/elt/gradedreaders